FUNDAMENTALS
OF MODERN MATHEMATICS

By J. M. Calloway

Department of Mathematics · Kalamazoo College, Kalamazoo, Michigan

ADDISON-WESLEY PUBLISHING COMPANY, INC.

READING, MASSACHUSETTS · PALO ALTO · LONDON

This book is in the

ADDISON-WESLEY SERIES IN MATHEMATICS

Consulting Editors

GAIL S. YOUNG AND RICHARD S. PIETERS

PREFACE

This book has been written in the belief that some understanding of *the nature of mathematics and the role that it plays in modern society* is essential for every liberally educated person.

The purpose of the book is to introduce the student to the world of mathematics—to help him to understand its nature, glimpse its beauty, sense its power, and discover its limitations. We want him to experience (at least second hand) the thrill of mathematical discovery, to appreciate the power and beauty of abstraction, and to get some feeling for the areas of application of mathematics. In addition we hope that he will come to understand the appropriate uses of mathematics and the role of the mathematician. It is by design that nothing has been said about developing skill in factoring, manipulating fractions, solving equations, and the like. We are not so concerned with developing facility in various techniques in mathematics as we are with having the reader understand the ideas which underlie these skills and having him see the consequences of these ideas and the ways in which they are useful.

We hope that it will be kept in mind, then, that it is a world of ideas which concerns us in this book, and not a mass of formulas, equations, and technical tricks.

Although there is enough material for a year's course meeting three times a week, the book was originally written for a one-term course of approximately 40 class meetings. Sufficient material is included to allow the instructor to choose those topics which are of most interest to him and to his students. The author feels that the aim of getting across the nature of mathematics does not depend on the topics chosen, but rather on the manner in which any particular subject is treated. The concepts considered should be fundamental ones, sharply defined and precisely used to develop in a clear, logical fashion some important part of mathematics.

One of the aims of this book is to develop and to encourage logical thinking, independence, and intellectual maturity. A calculated device to promote these qualities is the use of unfamiliar words before they are given precise mathematical definition. It is expected that the student will resort to an unabridged dictionary when he meets a word with which he is not familiar and that if the dictionary definition fails to help, he will look in the *Mathematics Dictionary* by Glenn and Robert C. James, 2nd ed., Van Nostrand, 1959.

Exercises marked "$^+$" either introduce a new term or extend the theory in some way. Those marked "*" are more difficult and sometimes demand some originality or ingenuity for their solution. Starred sections are optional and may be omitted without affecting the continuity of the text.

Experience obtained in three years of classroom testing of the material shows that if Chapters 1, 2, and 4 are studied, many patterns may be used in selecting topics from the remaining chapters, depending upon the taste and interests of the instructor and his students. For example, in a one-term course Chapters 1, 2, 4, and parts of Chapters 3, 7, and 8 may be selected. Another pattern consists of Chapters 1, 2, 3, 4, 5, and 6. Still another comprises Chapters 1, 2, 3, 4, 5, and 7.

Chapters 1 and 2 introduce the language of sets and the machinery from logic necessary to understand the statement of a mathematical theorem and its proof. Chapter 3 uses this machinery to indicate how the real number system may be developed by successive extensions, beginning with the natural numbers. Chapter 4 deals with the concept of function. Chapter 5 specializes the function concept to the study of sequences and introduces the notion of limit as applied to sequences and to continuous functions. Chapter 6 applies the limit concept to the two fundamental problems of the calculus, finding tangents and areas. Chapter 7 builds on the section on the natural numbers in Chapter 3, using the language of sets to study a few fundamental ideas in the theory of probability. Finally, Chapter 8 is an attempt to look at five mathematical systems axiomatically. It is hoped that this chapter will clearly set forth the modern view of mathematics as the study of abstract systems while at the same time exhibiting the varied applications which each such system may have.

While the immediate impetus for writing this book was the institution of a one-term graduation requirement in mathematics at Kalamazoo College, the ideas which emerged were conditioned by my association with Professor K. O. May over a period of years at Carleton College and by the use of his pioneering books in this area, *Elementary Analysis* and *Elements of Mathematics*. I gratefully acknowledge my debt to Professor May, as well as to the authors of many standard elementary texts, for the influence, both conscious and unconscious, which their works have had on my choice of material and method.

A special word of appreciation is due my colleague, Professor A. Frank Bausch, for his faithful reading of several versions of each of the chapters in the book and for his help both in the selection of topics and in the many detailed corrections and improvements which were made in the preliminary versions of the book.

My thanks also to my wife Anne Whitney Calloway who read the preliminary versions, argued forcefully for clarity and accuracy, prepared the index, and checked the answers to the problems.

I would also like to express my gratitude to the administration of Kalamazoo College for extending encouragement and financial support for the writing and the publication of the two preliminary versions of the text.

Finally my thanks to the many students who have cheerfully reacted, suggested, and suffered through earlier versions of the book. It was written for them.

Kalamazoo, Michigan   J. M. C.
April 1964

SUGGESTIONS FOR OUTSIDE READING

The author believes that frequently several versions of a topic can be very helpful to some students, not to all, but to some. For some students, seeing two versions of a topic only confuses the issue; but for the majority, coming at a subject from several slightly different points of view succeeds in clarifying many points which a single presentation may fail to do.

Consequently at the end of each chapter there are two lists, one of suggested outside readings which have been found to be directly helpful and worthwhile, and a second list of sources in which may be found a more extensive treatment or supplementary information on related subjects. It is suggested that the starred readings from the first list be made an integral part of the course. The unstarred readings in the first list give alternative versions of the material.

In addition, at the end of the book there is a general bibliography.

Since the purpose of this text is to explore the nature of mathematics and the role of mathematics and mathematicians, the following suggested readings are strongly recommended: 1, 2, 3, and 4 at the beginning of the course, and 5, 6, 7, and 8 at the end. These readings should help to place many of the specific topics in proper perspective and bring into focus details and symbols which may at times tend to overwhelm the student.

1. Roy Dubisch, *The Nature of Number*, Ch. 12, pp. 129–136, Ronald, 1952.
2. A. B. Evenson, *Modern Mathematics*, Ch. 1, pp. 1–8, Scott, 1962.
3. G. H. Hardy, "A Mathematician's Apology" from *The World of Mathematics* by James R. Newman, Vol. III, pp. 2024–2038.
4. John von Newman, "The Mathematician" from *The World of Mathematics* by James R. Newman, Vol. IV, pp. 2051–2063, Simon and Schuster, 1956, 1960.
5. M. Richardson, *Fundamentals of Mathematics*, Ch. 18, pp. 478–486, Macmillan, 1958.

6. E. C. TITCHMARSH, *Mathematics for the General Reader*, Ch. 15, pp. 192–197, Doubleday (Anchor Books), 1959.
7. MARSHALL H. STONE, "The Revolution in Mathematics," *The American Mathematical Monthly*, **68,** 8, Oct. 1961, pp. 715–734.
8. MINA REES, "The Nature of Mathematics," *The Mathematics Teacher*, **55,** 6, Oct. 1962, pp. 434–440.

CONTENTS

INTRODUCTION.   WHAT IS MATHEMATICS?   . .   1

1. SETS

1–1 Sets 3
1–2 Relations between sets and operations on sets . . . 7
1–3 Venn diagrams. 10
1–4 Sets and numbers 13
    Review exercises 16

2. MATHEMATICS AND LOGIC

2–1 Statements 19
2–2 Conditional statements 24
2–3 Axioms, definitions, and theorems 29
2–4 Rules of inference and mathematical proof 33
2–5 Methods of proof 35
*2–6 Quantified statements 40
    Review exercises 43

3. SETS OF NUMBERS

3–1 The natural numbers 46
3–2 Mathematical induction 49
3–3 The integers 51
3–4 The rational numbers 56
3–5 The real numbers 60
3–6 Summary 64
    Review exercises 65

4. RELATIONS AND FUNCTIONS

4–1 Relations 67
4–2 Variables, constants, and open sentences 71
4–3 Functions 73

4–4 Graphs of functions and relations 79
4–5 Converse of a relation and inverse functions 84
4–6 Linear functions and their graphs 86
*4–7 Polynomials *91
    Review exercises 93

5. SEQUENCES AND LIMITS

5–1 Sequences 95
5–2 The limit of a sequence 99
5–3 Real numbers as limits of sequences of rationals . . . 102
5–4 Limits of functions defined on the real numbers . . . 107
    Review exercises 111

6. THE CALCULUS

6–1 Introduction 114
6–2 The problem of tangents 114
6–3 The derivative 118
6–4 Applications to curve tracing 122
6–5 Area 127
6–6 The fundamental theorem of integral calculus . . . 133
6–7 Applications of the definite integral 135
6–8 Summary 140
    Review exercises 140

7. COUNTING AND PROBABILITY

7–1 Permutations and combinations 143
7–2 The binomial theorem 146
7–3 Probability 149
    Review exercises 154

8. MATHEMATICAL SYSTEMS

8–1 An axiom system 156
8–2 Groups 160
8–3 Boolean algebra 166
8–4 The boolean algebra {0, 1} 173
8–5 Fields 178
8–6 Conclusion 184

BIBLIOGRAPHY 186

LIST OF SYMBOLS 189

ANSWERS TO SELECTED EXERCISES 192

INDEX 209

INTRODUCTION

WHAT IS MATHEMATICS?

Since you have probably had some previous experience with mathematics, it would seem to be a fair question to ask, "What is mathematics?" If you give this question some thought, you probably feel pretty confident that you could tell whether or not a given printed page was mathematics. However, to define precisely the term "mathematics" is not nearly so easy. It is one of the aims of this book to lead you to a better understanding of the nature of mathematics and the work of mathematicians.

In the suggested outside readings, you will encounter several answers to the question, "What is mathematics?" Some people contend that it is the most abstract of the sciences, others that it is more nearly akin to the arts of music, painting, and poetry. Still others pretend that it is only an elaborate game, played according to arbitrarily made-up rules. The British philosopher and mathematician Bertrand Russell once said, "... mathematics may be defined as the subject in which we never know what we are talking about, nor whether what we are saying is true." This rather shocking statement contains more truth than one might suppose. The sense in which it is true will become much clearer later on. At any rate most people agree that it is a language ideally suited to the precise statement of complicated ideas. This is the reason that mathematics has become the universally accepted language of science. Of course, mathematics is more than a mere language; it has its own literature containing many of the finest and purest creations of the human mind.

One of the distinguishing features of modern mathematics is its interest in the foundations and the logical structure of the subject. In fact, another of the views about mathematics is that mathematics is simply the recognition of patterns. In this view, the job of the mathe-

1

matician is to recognize and abstract from dissimilar situations the elements which these situations have in common. Once these properties, usually called axioms of the system, have been selected, the mathematician proceeds to prove that certain conclusions follow from these assumptions. For example, "If n is a positive integer, then the sum of the first n positive integers is $n(n + 1)/2$," and "If $x^2 = 2$, then x is not a rational number," are typical mathematical statements. These are propositions which may be proved by a series of logical arguments based on a set of axioms for the natural numbers (that is, the counting numbers 1, 2, 3, . . .). These statements can be shown to be logical consequences of the axioms and definitions which are a part of this mathematical structure. We will consider this subject in greater detail in Chapters 2 and 3.

1 | SETS

1–1 SETS

We must begin somewhere, and you might suppose that we should begin with numbers. However it can be argued that the concept of number depends on the notion of a set. The set idea is so familiar that you probably have never given it much thought. By a *set* we simply mean a *collection of objects*. For a set to be determined, we need to be able to decide, given any object, whether or not it belongs to the set: for example, the set of books in the Library of Congress, or the set of faculty members of Kalamazoo College, or the set of students who scored more than 700 on the College Entrance Board Examination in mathematics, or the set of freshmen with four eyes and three legs. Given any object, it is pretty easy to tell whether or not the object belongs to any one of the given sets.

There are two important things to notice about this idea of a set. One is that the set itself is an object which is different from any of its members. The set is the whole collection and is the object consisting of all its members. The second is that given any object, we must be able to decide whether or not the object belongs to the set. For example, the National League is a set of baseball teams, and certainly any baseball fan would know whether or not the Tigers belong to this set. Incidentally, each member of the National League is a set, a set of players. The First Division and the cellar are also sets of teams

3

which are contained in the original set. Now the cellar has only one member, that team which happens to be in the cellar. However, the team and the cellar are not the same thing; the cellar is the set and the team in the cellar is the only member of the set. Another example is the set of living female presidents of the United States. This is a perfectly good set; however, it doesn't happen to have any members. In all cases, we wish to distinguish between the set and its members.

In what is to follow it will be convenient to have some systematic way to denote sets and members of sets. In the examples which we have considered so far, we have described the set by a statement which gave the condition for membership in the set—the set of books in the Library of Congress or the set of living female presidents of the United States. Another way is simply to list the elements. For example, A is the set consisting of the numbers 1, 5, and 7. The traditional way of denoting this set is $A = \{1, 5, 7\}$. If a set can be described by listing all its members, we may denote the set by simply enclosing the list in braces.

$B = \{\text{John F. Kennedy}\}$

$C = \{\text{H. C. H., F. D. R., H. S. T., D. D. E., J. F. K., L. B. J.}\}$

$D = \{\text{Falla, Checkers, Strelka}\}$

The so-called *roster notation* which we have used to denote a set by listing its members is not always convenient. Suppose that we wanted to consider the set E of all even positive integers. The trouble here is that we are unable to list all the members of E, since our list would never end. An alternative notation is the following: $E = \{x \mid x \text{ is an even positive integer}\}$. We read this, "$E$ is the set of all x's such that x is an even positive integer."

Let us consider another example: $F = \{x \mid x^2 = 2\}$ (read F is the set of all numbers x such that x^2 equals 2). Within the parentheses we have added the word numbers (all numbers x, such that . . .). The fact that x stands for a number is understood from the context. We usually have in mind a large set from which we select the elements to form a given set. For example, in sets B and C above, it might be the set of all people, in D the set of all dogs, and in A and E and F the set of all numbers. This large set which is usually clear from the context is called the *universe of discourse* or, more briefly, the *universal set, U*. The set which contains no members, e.g., the set of living female presidents, is called the *empty set* or the *null set*, and is denoted by the symbol $\emptyset$.

Our notation for membership in a set is as follows: $1 \in S$, read "1 belongs to S," "1 is an element of the set S," or "1 is a member of the set S." For example, $1 \in \{1, 5, 7\}$, read "1 belongs to the set whose members are 1, 5, and 7." The symbols $\emptyset$ and $\in$ illustrate the common use in mathematics of special symbols in situations in which Roman letters would be confusing or inconvenient. We occasionally want to make statements such as "2 does not belong to the set S," or "2 is not an element of S." Our notation for either of these statements is "$2 \notin S$."

In this section we have been concerned principally with three ideas: set, element, and belongs to. These are really undefined terms. By illustrations and by talking about these ideas, we try to convey how they will be used; however, their logical status in our mathematical structure of sets remains that of undefined terms. We now have a convenient notation for designating sets and for indicating membership in a set. In addition, we have defined the sets U (the universal set) and $\emptyset$ (the empty set).

In succeeding sections, we shall discuss relations between sets and operations on sets and indicate how these ideas are helpful in mathematics.

EXERCISES

1. List some members (as many as three, if possible) of each of the following sets:

  (a) The set of letters in the Greek alphabet.
  (b) The set of Nobel prize winners.
  (c) The set of countries not belonging to the United Nations.
  (d) The set of foreign-born presidents of the United States.
  (e) $\{x \mid x + x = 2x\}$.
  (f) $\{x \mid 3x + 2 = 4x\}$.
  (g) $\{x \mid 3x + 2 = 3x\}$.
  (h) $\{x \mid (x - 1)(x + 1) = x^2 - 1\}$.
  (i) $\{x \mid x^2 = 4\}$.
  (j) $\{x \mid x \text{ is a rational number}\}$.
  (k) The set of states east of the Mississippi River.
  (l) The set of cities in the United States with populations greater than one million.

2. Write in the roster notation:

  (a) The set of all integers which are larger than -4 and are smaller than 2.

(b) The set of all positive proper fractions with denominator 5.
(c) The set of all United States senators from the state of Michigan.
(d) The set of all even numbers greater than 6 and less than 8.
(e) The set of all living ex-presidents of the United States.

3. Denote the set $\{x \mid x$ is an integer and $x^2 = x\}$ in another way.

4. Given the sets $A = \{-2, -1, 0, 1, 2\}$, $B = \{x \mid x$ is a positive integer$\}$, $C = \{x \mid x$ is a rational number$\}$, $D = \{x \mid x$ is a real number$\}$. Which of the following belong to A? to B? to C? to D? to A and to B? to A or to B? $-1, 5, 2, \sqrt{2}, -2 -\sqrt{2}, \sqrt{-2}, \pi, \frac{3}{2}, \sqrt{19}, \frac{17}{19}, 4\frac{2}{3}, \frac{-6}{3}$.

5. Is $\{1, 2\} \in \{\{1, 2, 7\}, 1, 2, \{1, 7\}\}$? Explain your answer.

6. How many members does the set $\{0\}$ contain? Is $\{0\} = \emptyset$?

7. Is $\{0\} \in \{0\}$? Is $\{0\} \in \{\{0\}, 0\}$?

8. In each of the following, the universal set and a certain described set are specified. Decide whether the described set is the universal set, the empty set, or neither.

(a) All United States presidents born in Virginia. (U is the set of all United States presidents.)
(b) All United States presidents who were naturalized citizens. (U is the set of all United States presidents.)
(c) All voters under 21 years of age. (U is the set of all Michigan voters.)
(d) $\{x \mid x \cdot 1 = x\}$. (U is the set of all numbers.)
(e) $\{x \mid x^2 > 0\}$. (U is the set of all numbers.)
(f) $\{x \mid x \cdot 0 \neq 0\}$. ($U$ is the set of all numbers.)
(g) $\{x \mid x + (-x) = 0\}$. (U is the set of all numbers.)
(h) $\{1, 3, 5, 7, 9\}$. (U is the set of all odd numbers less than 10.)

9. What property do the following sets have in common? $A = \{1, 2, 3\}$, $B = \{0, -1, 12\}$, $C = \{$Caroline, John, Jackie$\}$, and $D = \{0, \{0\}, \{0, 1\}\}$.

10. Define by some appropriate property:

(a) A set which has as its only element the state of Michigan.
(b) A set of integers (whole numbers) which will consist only of the integer 2.
(c) A set of numbers which will consist only of the positive odd integers.

11. Describe in words the following sets:

    (a) $\{1, 2, 3, 4, 5\}$.

    (b) $\{2, 4, 8, 16\}$.

    (c) $\{2, 6, 10, 14, 18, 22\}$.

    (d) $\{-\frac{2}{3}, -\frac{1}{3}, 0, \frac{1}{3}, \frac{2}{3}\}$.

    (e) {Maine, Maryland, Massachusetts, Michigan, Minnesota, Mississippi, Missouri, Montana}.

12. Are sets $A = \{1, 2\}$ and $B = \{1, 2, 1\}$ the same set or are they different? Explain.

1–2 RELATIONS BETWEEN SETS AND OPERATIONS ON SETS

In Exercise 12 of the previous section you were asked whether the set $A = \{1, 2\}$ is the same as the set $B = \{1, 2, 1\}$. To clarify this question we make the following definition:

Definition 1–2.1. Two sets A and B are *equal* $(A = B)$ if and only if every element of A is an element of B and every element of B is an element of A.

According to this definition for the sets A and B above, $A = B$, since 1 and 2, the elements of A, belong to B, and every element of B belongs to A.

Whenever we use the symbol $=$ we shall mean that the two symbols appearing before and after the equality sign are simply two names for the same thing. Thus in the case of sets, when we write $S = \{1, 2\}$, we mean that S is simply a name for the set whose elements are the numbers 1 and 2; or when we write $S = T$, we mean that S and T are two names for the same set.

Besides equality, there are other possible relations between sets. For example, consider $C = \{1, 2\}$ and $D = \{1, 2, 3\}$. Every element of C is an element of D, but not every element of D is an element of C.

Definition 1–2.2. A is a *subset* of B $(A \subset B)$, if and only if every element of A is an element of B. We write $A \subset B$, which may be read, "A is a subset of B" or "A is contained in B."

According to this definition, in any given discussion, every set is a subset of the universal set U. Also the empty set, $\emptyset$, is trivially a subset of every set. For if $\emptyset$ were not a subset of a given set A, this would mean that there was an element in $\emptyset$ which was not an element of A. Since there are no elements in $\emptyset$, it is impossible to find such an element. Accordingly, we say that $\emptyset$ is a subset of every set. It is important to remember the distinction between a set and its members. For example, $\{1, 2\} \subset \{1, 2, 3\}$, but $\{1, 2\}$ is not a subset of $\{\{1, 2\}, 1\}$, since $2 \notin \{\{1, 2\}, 1\}$. However, $\{1, 2\} \in \{\{1, 2\}, 1\}$. The symbol $\in$ is used to denote membership in a set and is therefore a relation between an element of a set and the set itself, while $\subset$ indicates a relation between two sets. Set notation is used correctly in $1 \in \{1, 2\}$ and $\{1\} \subset \{1, 2\}$ but not in $\{1\} \in \{1, 2, 3\}$ and $1 \subset \{1, 2\}$.

It has probably occurred to you that given two sets A and B, it is possible that $A \neq B$ and also that neither $A \subset B$ nor $B \subset A$. For example, suppose that $A = \{1\}$, $B = \{2, 3\}$, and $C = \{2, 4\}$. If two nonempty sets have no elements in common, we say that the sets are *disjoint*. Sets A and B are disjoint, as are A and C. However, B and C are not disjoint, and neither one is a subset of the other, nor are they equal. Sometimes we would like to talk about the common elements of two sets.

Definition 1–2.3. The *intersection* of two sets A and B is the set of elements common to both sets. We write $C = A \cap B$, read "C is the intersection of A and B."

For example, from the sets B and C above, we form

$$D = \{2\} = B \cap C.$$

Definition 1–2.4. The *union* of two sets A and B is the set consisting of all the elements which belong either to set A or to set B (or to both). We write $C = A \cup B$, read "C is the union of A and B."

For example, $\{2, 3, 4\} = \{2, 3\} \cup \{2, 4\}$.

You may have noticed that while $=$ and $\subset$ were used to express propositions about sets given in advance, $\cap$ and $\cup$ were used to form new sets from given sets. Accordingly, we say that $=$ and $\subset$ denote *relations* between sets and that $\cap$ and $\cup$ denote *operations* on sets (more specifically, binary relations and binary operations, since they apply only to sets considered two at a time).

EXERCISES

1. True or false:
    (a) $\{1\} \in \{1, 2\}$.   (b) $\{1\} \subset \{1, 2\}$.   (c) $\{1\} \subset \{\{1\}, 2\}$.
    (d) $\{0\} = \emptyset$.   (e) $\emptyset \subset \{0\}$.

2. Prove that there is only one empty set; that is, show that if A is a set with no elements and B is a set with no elements, $A = B$. We denote this unique empty set by $\emptyset$.

$^{+}$3. Make a list of all the subsets of
    (a) $\{1, 2, 3\}$.   (b) $\{0, a, 1, b\}$.   (c) $\{0, \{1\}\}$.
The new set whose members are the subsets of the original set is called the *power set* of the original set. How many elements are there in the power set of a set with n elements?

4. Given $A = \{a, b, c\}$, $B = \{b\}$, $C = \{a, c\}$, find
    (a) $A \cap B$.   (b) $A \cap A$.   (c) $A \cup A$.
    (d) $A \cap \emptyset$.   (e) $A \cup \emptyset$.   (f) $A \cup B$.
    (g) $A \cap C$.   (h) $B \cup C$.   (i) $B \cap C$.

5. For the sets A, B, and C in Exercise 4:
    (a) Is $A \subset C$?   (b) Is $B \subset C$?   (c) Does $b \in A$?
    (d) Is $B \subset A$?   (e) Is $(B \cap C) \subset \emptyset$?

6. How are the following sets related? (That is, are the sets disjoint or is one a subset of another?)
    (a) The set E of even numbers; the set 0 of odd numbers.
    (b) The set S of squares; the set R of rectangles.
    (c) $\{a, b, c\}$; $\{d, e\}$.
    (d) $\{a, b, c\}$; $\{b, c\}$.
    (e) The set of women; the set of mothers; the set of college graduates who are grandmothers.

7. Prove: $A \cap B = A$ if and only if $A \subset B$; that is:
    (a) Show that if $A \cap B = A$, then $A \subset B$;
    (b) Show that if $A \subset B$, then $A \cap B = A$.

8. Prove:
    (a) $A \cap B = B \cap A$.   (b) $A \cup B = B \cup A$.

$^{+}$9. Given a set, A, in a universe, U, the set of elements in U which are not in A is called the *complement* of A, written $\overline{A}$. If U is the set of all natural

---

$^{+}$ Exercises marked by the symbol $^{+}$ either introduce a new term or extend the theory in some way.

numbers, E is the set of even numbers, and P is the set of primes, describe the following sets:

(a) $\bar{E}$.   (b) $\bar{E} \cap E$.   (c) $\bar{P}$.

(d) $\bar{P} \cup P$.   (e) $E \cap P$.   (f) $\overline{(E \cup P)}$.

(g) $\bar{E} \cup \bar{P}$.

10. Are the sets in (a) and (g) of Exercise 9 equal? disjoint? If not, how are they related?

11. Express the following subsets of U in simpler terms:

$$\bar{\emptyset}, \qquad \bar{U}, \qquad A \cup \bar{U}, \qquad A \cap \bar{\emptyset}, \qquad A \cap \bar{U}.$$

⁺12. If every element of A is a member of B and there is at least one element of B which is not a member of A, we say that A is a *proper subset* of B. (Sometimes different symbols are used for subset and proper subset. In this case, subset is denoted by $\subseteq$ and proper subset by $\subset$.) Name all the proper subsets of:

(a) $\{0, 1, 2\}$.

(b) $S = \{x \mid x^2 = 2 \text{ or } x - 3 = 0\}$.

(c) $T = \{x \mid x \text{ is an integer}, x > 1, x < 5\}$.

1–3 VENN DIAGRAMS

A convenient device for visualizing relations between sets is the Venn diagram. We represent the universal set, U, by a set of points within a large rectangle. Other sets are represented by sets of points within circles or some other convenient closed curves. For example, in Fig. 1–1, it is clear from the diagram that $A \subset B$. In Fig. 1–2 $A \cap B = \emptyset$.

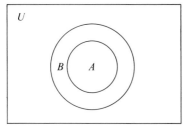
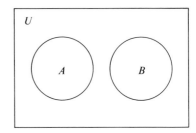

FIGURE 1–1   FIGURE 1–2

In Fig. 1–3 the crosshatched region represents $A \cap B$.

The complement, $\bar{A}$, of a set, A (see Section 1–2, Exercise 9), is the set of points in U but not in A (Fig 1–4).

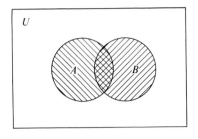

FIGURE 1-3

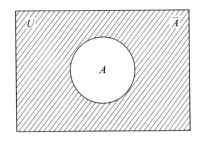

FIGURE 1-4

Some of the results of operations on sets are easier to understand when Venn diagrams are used. For example,

$$A \cup (B \cap C) = (A \cup B) \cap (A \cup C).$$

The left-hand side of the equation may be represented by the diagrams in Fig. 1-5. It can be seen from the sequence of diagrams in Fig. 1-6 that the right-hand side, represented by the crosshatched region, is clearly the same set.

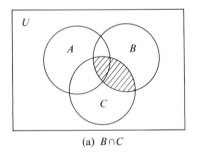

(a) $B \cap C$

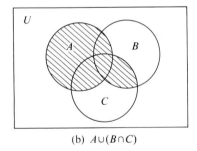

(b) $A \cup (B \cap C)$

FIGURE 1-5

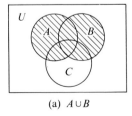

(a) $A \cup B$

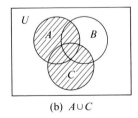

(b) $A \cup C$

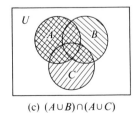

(c) $(A \cup B) \cap (A \cup C)$

FIGURE 1-6

EXERCISES

1. Make Venn diagrams containing sets A and B which show that:

   (a) $B \subset A$.   (b) $A \cap B \neq \emptyset$.   (c) $A \cap B = \emptyset$.

   (d) $A \cup B \neq U$.   (e) $A \subset (A \cup B)$.   (f) $(A \cup B) \subset B$.

   (g) $B \subset (A \cap B)$.

2. Make a sequence of diagrams showing that

$$A \cap (B \cup C) = (A \cap B) \cup (A \cap C)$$

for any sets A, B, and C.

3. None of the statements below is true of all sets P, Q, and R. In each case, make a diagram which contradicts the statement.

   (a) If $P \subset Q$, then $Q \subset P$.

   (b) If P and Q are disjoint and Q and R are disjoint, then P and R are disjoint.

   (c) If $P \cap Q \neq \emptyset$ and $Q \cap R \neq \emptyset$, then $P \cap R \neq \emptyset$.

   (d) If $P \cap Q \neq \emptyset$, then $P = Q$.

⁺4. Make Venn diagrams which show that for any sets A and B,

   $\overline{A \cup B} = \overline{A} \cap \overline{B}$ and $\overline{A \cap B} = \overline{A} \cup \overline{B}$ (De Morgan's Laws).

5. Make a Venn diagram to illustrate the relationships between the positive integers, the integers, the rational numbers, and the real numbers.

6. For the Venn diagram below, indicate each of the following sets by shading the appropriate region.

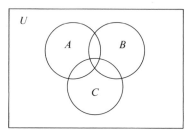

FIGURE 1-7

   (a) $A \cap B$.   (b) $A \cup C$.   (c) $A \cap (B \cup C)$.

   (d) $A \cup (B \cup C)$.   (e) $(A \cap B) \cup C$.   (f) $(A \cup B) \cap (A \cup C)$.

   (g) $\overline{A} \cap B$.   (h) $\overline{A \cup C} \cap B$.   (i) $\overline{A \cap B} \cup C$.

   (j) $A \cap (B \cap C)$.   (k) $(A \cap B) \cap \overline{B}$.

7. Draw Venn diagrams to show:

   (a) $A \cup B = (A \cap \overline{B}) \cup B$.

   (b) $(A \cap \overline{B}) \cap B = \emptyset$.

   (c) $A = (A \cap B) \cup (A \cap \overline{B})$.

1–4 SETS AND NUMBERS

In Section 1–1 we mentioned that an argument could be made for the idea that the notion of a set is more basic than that of number. In fact, suppose that you wanted to explain to a Martian or to a three-year-old brother or sister what the number three is. You might hold up three fingers or you might put three small stones together and point to them and say, "Three". You might pull three pennies from your pocket or line up three tools from your tool kit. If you have ever tried this sort of thing, you may have found that there are many attributes that these collections have beside "threeness." In fact, if the stones were brown, the pennies were old copper ones, and you had a good tan, the Martian and the three-year-old might understandably think three meant brown (that is, if Martians are able to distinguish colors). As a matter of fact, three is a very abstract idea; it is just the one property that all sets containing three objects have in common. All the sets mentioned above may consist of round objects, all may consist of brown objects, but if you can imagine the collection consisting of *all* sets of three objects, the one attribute they all have in common is *threeness*. Thus the recognition of properties of sets is really necessary before the abstract notion of three can be formulated.

However, this abstract notion of threeness is not necessary for many purposes. For example, a person who knows nothing about counting or about numbers can tell whether the number of persons in a room is the same as the number of chairs. He simply asks everyone to sit down. If there are no persons standing and no empty chairs, then the number of persons is the same as the number of chairs. This process of matching one set (the set of persons) with another set (the set of chairs) is essentially what happens when we count. We match one set, the set of objects being counted, with another set, the set of natural numbers it takes to count the given set.

The mathematical way of describing this pairing process is to say that we "set up a *one-to-one correspondence* between two sets." We say that any set whose members can be put into a one-to-one correspondence with the set $\{1, 2, 3\}$ has *three* members.

EXAMPLE.

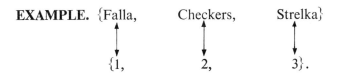

Definition 1–4.1. Two sets A and B are said to be *equivalent* if and only if a one-to-one correspondence can be set up between the two sets.

For example, the sets $\{0, 1, 2\}$ and $\{a, b\}$ are not equivalent. We may let a correspond to 0, 1, or 2. If a corresponds to 0, then b must correspond either to 1 or 2. If a corresponds to 1, then b must correspond to 0 or 2. If a corresponds to 2, b must correspond to either 0 or 1. Thus in every case there is always an element of the first set which has no correspondent in the second set, and it is impossible to set up a one-to-one correspondence between the two sets.

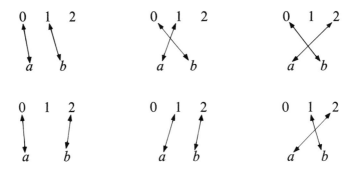

Definition 1–4.2. A *nonempty* set is said to be *finite* if there exists a natural number n such that the given set is equivalent to the set of natural numbers $\{1, 2, 3, \ldots, n\}$,† that is, a set consisting of the natural numbers 1, 2, 3, and so on, up to and including the number n. Otherwise, we say that the nonempty set is *infinite*. The empty set is considered to be a finite set.

For two finite sets A and B, the statement that set A contains the same number of elements as set B may be true or false, but in either case it is a meaningful statement. However, if two sets are infinite, this statement is ambiguous, to say the least. For instance, the set of even natural numbers is equivalent to the set of all natural numbers, since if we represent the even numbers by

$$E = \{x \mid x = 2n, n \text{ a natural number}\} = \{2, 4, 6, 8, \ldots, 2n, \ldots\}$$

---

† In mathematics the symbol $\ldots$ (an ellipsis) is frequently used to indicate that terms are omitted. In all such cases the omitted terms are assumed to be obviously understood, and the symbol may be read "and so on."

and the set of natural numbers by $N = \{1, 2, 3, \ldots, n, \ldots\}$, we may set up the one-to-one correspondence

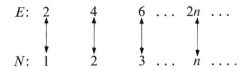

In one sense, there are just as many even natural numbers as there are natural numbers. We were able to pair them off so that every element of E has a correspondent in N, and conversely. On the other hand, every even natural number is a natural number, but there are natural numbers which are not even, say 1, 3, 5, etc. From this point of view, one might say that since E is a proper subset of N, there are certainly more numbers in N than in E. In fact, since we can set up a one-to-one correspondence between E and the set of numbers which are in N but not in E, namely $2n \leftrightarrow 2n - 1$, one might reasonably say that there are about twice as many numbers in N as in E.

These added complications are not present for finite sets. In fact, for finite sets, a proper subset of a finite set is never equivalent to the set itself. However, the surprising fact, which turns out to be characteristic for infinite sets, is that every infinite set has a proper subset which can be put into one-to-one correspondence with the set itself.

It should also be noted that very large is not at all the same as infinite. A set with 16 trillion elements might be considered very large, but it is clearly finite and can be put into one-to-one correspondence with the set $S = \{1, 2, 3, \ldots, 16{,}000{,}000{,}000{,}000\}$.

EXERCISES

1. Are the following sets finite or infinite?
    (a) The set of all citizens of the United States.
    (b) The set of all integers divisible by 17.
    (c) The set of all grains of sand on all the beaches in the world.
    (d) The set of all molecules in a glass of water.
    (e) The set of all stars in our galaxy.

2. Give three examples of infinite sets.

3. Are the following pairs of sets equivalent? If so, pair off the elements.
    (a) $\{1, 2, 3, \ldots, 20\}$, $\{2, 4, 6, \ldots, 40\}$.
    (b) $\{1, 2, 3, 4, 5, 6, 7, 8, 9, 10\}$, $\{20, 22, 24, \ldots, 40\}$.
    (c) $\{1, 2, 3, \ldots, n, \ldots\}$, $\{1, 3, 5, \ldots, 2n - 1, \ldots\}$.

*(d) {natural numbers}, {rational numbers}.

*(e) {all points on a ruler between 1 and 2}, {all points on a ruler between 3 and 4}.

*(f) {the points on a line segment one inch long}, {the points on a line segment one foot long}.

4. Are the sets {0, 1, 2} and {1, 2, 3} equivalent? are they equal? Explain.

5. Are the following sets equivalent? equal?

    (a) {1, 2, 3, 4, 5}, $\{x \mid x$ is a positive integer and $x < 6\}$.

    (b) {2, 5}, $\{x \mid x^2 - 7x + 10 = 0\}$.

    (c) {3, 5, 6, 11, 13}, $\{x \mid x$ is prime and $x < 6\}$.

6. Are the sets $\{1, 2, 3, \ldots, n, \ldots\}$ and $\{2, 3, 4, \ldots, n + 1, \ldots\}$ equivalent? are they equal?

REVIEW EXERCISES

Given: $N = \{x \mid x$ is a natural number$\}$, $I = \{x \mid x$ is an integer$\}$, $Q = \{x \mid x$ is a rational number$\}$, and $R = \{x \mid x$ is a real number$\}$.

1. Which of the following belong to N? to I? to Q? to R?

$$1, \quad \tfrac{2}{3}, \quad \tfrac{\sqrt{7}}{3}, \quad \sqrt{2}, \quad -3, \quad 0, \quad \tfrac{17}{19}, \quad \pi.$$

2. Denote the following sets as simply as possible. (Take $U = R$, the set of all real numbers.)

    (a) $N \cup I$.   (b) $N \cap I$.   (c) $Q \cup \overline{R}$.

    (d) $\overline{N} \cap I$.   (e) $\overline{Q} \cap N$.   (f) $R \cap I$.

3. Are the following true or false?

    (a) $1 \in \{\{1\}, 0\}$.   (b) $\{1\} \subset \{\{1\}, 0\}$.   (c) $\{1\} \in \{\{1\}, 0\}$.

    (d) $N \subset I$.   (e) $\emptyset \subset N$.

4. Given the sets $A = \{0, 1\}$, $B = \{a, b\}$, $C = \{0, a, b\}$:

    (a) Is A equal to B?

    (b) Is B equivalent to A?

    (c) Are A and B disjoint?

    (d) What is $A \cap B$? $A \cap C$? $B \cap C$?

    (e) What is $B \cap (A \cup C)$? $B \cup C$? $B \cup (A \cap C)$?

5. Given the universe $U = \{0, 1, 2, 3, 4, 5, 6, 7\}$, $A = \{0, 1, 2, 3\}$, and $B = \{0, 5, 6, 7\}$. What is:

    (a) $A \cap B$?   (b) $\overline{A} \cup B$?   (c) $A \cap \overline{B}$?

    (d) $\{x \mid (x + 4) \in B\}$?   (e) $\{x \mid x \in A$ or $x \in B\}$?

---

* Exercises marked by an asterisk (*) are more difficult and may demand some originality or ingenuity.

6. Let the universe U be the set of natural numbers, A be the set of prime numbers, B be the set of odd numbers. Are the following true or false?

(a) $A \cap B \neq \emptyset$.
(b) $\overline{A} \cap B = \emptyset$.
(c) $A \subset \overline{B}$.
(d) $\{x \mid x \in A \text{ and } x \in \overline{B}\} \neq \emptyset$.

7. If U is the set of all people, A the set of all males, B the set of all people over 6 feet tall, and C the set of all people with blue eyes; then what denotes:

(a) The set of all females?
(b) The set of all people over 6 feet tall and male?
(c) The set of blue-eyed females?
(d) The set of all blue-eyed males of height less than or equal to 6 feet?

8. Let the universe U be the set of natural numbers, and let A and B be subsets thereof. Are the following true or false?

(a) If A and B are finite, then $A \cup B$ is finite.
(b) If A is finite, then $\overline{A}$ is finite.
(c) If A is infinite, then $\overline{A}$ is infinite.
(d) If A is infinite, then $A \cup B$ is infinite.

9. In a Venn diagram containing sets A and B, shade:

(a) $A \cup \overline{B}$. (b) $A \cap \overline{B}$. (c) $\overline{A} \cup \overline{B}$.
(d) $\overline{A \cup B}$. (e) $\overline{A} \cap \overline{B}$. (f) $\overline{A \cap B}$.

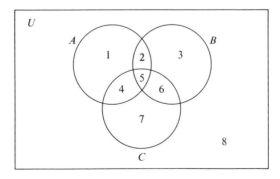

FIGURE 1-8

10. In the Venn diagram above, U is partitioned into 8 disjoint subsets as indicated. Find an expression in terms of sets, A, B, and C for each numbered subset. For example, the subset numbered 5 is $(A \cap B) \cap C$.

Suggested Readings

*LUCE, R. D., "Some Basic Mathematical Concepts" in *Studies in Mathematics*, Vol. I, School Mathematics Study Group, Yale University, New Haven, Conn., 1959, Ch. 1, pp. 7–31, pp. 37–45.

*RUSSELL, B., "Definition of Number" in *The World of Mathematics* edited by James R. Newman, Simon and Schuster, New York, 1956, Vol. I, pp. 537–543.

EVENSON, A. B., *Modern Mathematics*, Scott, Foresman and Co., Chicago, 1962, Ch. 2, pp. 9–22.

FUJII, J. N., *An Introduction to the Elements of Mathematics*, John Wiley, New York, 1961, Ch. 6, pp. 69–84.

KEMENY, J. G., J. L. SNELL, and G. L. THOMPSON, *Introduction to Finite Mathematics*, Prentice-Hall, Englewood Cliffs, N. J., 1957, Ch. 2, pp. 54–63.

TITCHMARSH, E. C., *Mathematics for the General Reader*, Doubleday Anchor Books, Garden City, N. Y., 1959, Ch. 1, pp. 13–19.

General References

CHRISTIAN, R. R., *Introduction to Logic and Sets*, Ginn and Co., Toronto, 1958.

KAMKE, E., *The Theory of Sets*, Dover Publications, Inc., New York, 1950.

NCTM Twenty-third Yearbook, *Insights into Modern Mathematics*, "Operating With Sets" by E. J. McShane, NCTM, Washington, 1957, pp. 36–64.

2 | MATHEMATICS AND LOGIC

2–1 STATEMENTS

In the introduction, we mentioned as one of the virtues of mathematics that it is a language in which one may express complicated ideas with great precision. We also maintain that if a mathematical argument is clearly presented, all reasonable persons who accept the axioms and the rules of proof on which it is based can agree as to the validity of the argument. This process of systematic reasoning from clearly stated assumptions according to precisely stated rules is the essence of mathematics. The formal theory associated with this process is called logic. Accordingly, it might be said with some justification that much of mathematics is part of logic. However, the interests of mathematicians and logicians are generally quite different. At any rate, some understanding of the basic ideas and terms of symbolic logic is useful for our work in mathematics. For this reason we devote this chapter to a brief look at that subject.

A careful exposition of symbolic logic would take far more time than we can afford in this book. Necessarily, then, the following picture will often be greatly oversimplified. References to more extended versions of this material will be found in the list of suggested readings at the end of the chapter.

To begin with, we are concerned with various ways of combining statements. It might seem strange that we should immediately concern ourselves with combinations of statements rather than with single "simple" statements. However, it will become clear that our interest is not so much in the truth of a single statement as in whether one statement follows from a sequence of other statements. By a *statement* we mean *a sentence which is either true or false, but not both.* Some sentences fail to meet this condition, for example, the sentence, "This sentence is false." If we say that the sentence is true, then it is false.

If, on the other hand, we claim that the sentence is false, then it is true. Such sentences will not be considered mathematical statements.

Given several statements (sentences which are either true or false but not both), we wish to set up rules by which we can decide the truth of various combinations of the given statements. Many new statements are formed by using the connectives "not," "and," "or."

Given a statement p, its *negation* is the statement not-p. For example, if p is "All men are bald," then not-p is "Not all men are bald," or "It is not the case that all men are bald." We shall denote the negation of a statement p by $\sim p$, read "not p."

Given two statements p and q, the statement "p and q" is called the *conjunction* of p and q, and we shall denote the conjunction by $p \wedge q$. For example,

> p: It is hot.
>
> q: I am going swimming.
>
> $p \wedge q$: It is hot and I am going swimming.

Finally, "p or q," written $p \vee q$, is called the *disjunction* of p and q. For example,

> p: John is a freshman.
>
> q: John is a sophomore.
>
> $p \vee q$: John is a freshman or John is a sophomore.

Our object now is to decide, given the truth status of p and q, the truth or falsity of $\sim p$, $p \wedge q$, and $p \vee q$. We use a convenient device called a *truth table* to state these results, which may be thought of as axioms of logic.

NEGATION

p	$\sim p$
T	F
F	T

▲

CONJUNCTION

p	q	$p \wedge q$
T	T	T
T	F	F
F	T	F
F	F	F

▲

DISJUNCTION

p	q	$p \vee q$
T	T	T
T	F	T
F	T	T
F	F	F

▲

The first two of these axioms seem quite natural. If a statement p is true, its negation is false. If the statement is false, its negation is true. For $p \wedge q$ to be true, both p and q must be true. If either one is false, we say that the conjunction is false.

The table for disjunction may not seem so natural at first glance. Certainly if either p is true and q is false, or if p is false and q is true, we would say that $p \vee q$ is true. And if both p and q are false, it would seem clear that the disjunction is not true. However, to call the disjunction true if both p and q are true may seem arbitrary. But in ordinary usage, the sense of *or* is not always clear. For example, "I like chocolate ice cream or vanilla" means I like either one and perhaps both flavors. On the other hand, "I will take either Mathematics I or English I at 9:00" means one or the other, but not both. In mathematical logic, if we wish to distinguish between these cases, we use a different symbol, $\veebar$, for the "exclusive disjunction." Below is the truth table for exclusive disjunction. In general, however, we use *or* to mean inclusive disjunction and use the table for $\vee$ as the axiom which gives the truth value of a disjunction.

p	q	$p \veebar q$
T	T	F
T	F	T
F	T	T
F	F	F

▲

A few remarks about what we have said are now in order. We have in this section on logic agreed to attach labels "true" and "false" to certain *compound* statements, that is, statements formed from other statements. We are not interested at the moment in the truth of any particular simple statement; we merely agree

    (1) to consider only sentences to which a label "true" or "false" may be attached (i.e., statements), and

    (2) once the labels have been given to the simple statements, to use our axioms (given by the truth tables) to decide what label to attach to the new statement.

We are now in a position to construct truth tables from which we may determine labels for more complicated statements by applying systematically the axioms for negation, conjunction, and disjunction. In constructing these tables we consider all possible combinations of truth values for the simple component statements. If only one simple statement is involved, the truth table will contain two rows. For example, to determine the truth value of the statement $p \lor \sim p$, we need consider only the two cases, p is true and p is false.

p	$\sim p$	$p \lor \sim p$
T	F	T
F	T	T

▲

The disjunction $p \lor \sim p$ always has the truth value T, regardless of the truth status of the statement p itself.

To construct a table for a compound statement containing two simple statements, p and q, we need four rows. If p is true, q is either true or false; if p is false, q is either true or false.

For example, if we are interested in the truth value of $\sim(p \land \sim q)$, the table on the left tells us the correct label in all possible cases.

p	q	$\sim q$	$p \land \sim q$	$\sim(p \land \sim q)$
T	T	F	F	T
T	F	T	T	F
F	T	F	F	T
F	F	T	F	T
1	2	3	4	5

▲

p	q	$\sim(p \land \sim q)$
T	T	$T\ T\ F\ F\ T$
T	F	$F\ T\ T\ T\ F$
F	T	$T\ F\ F\ F\ T$
F	F	$T\ F\ F\ T\ F$
1	2	5\ 1\ 4\ 3\ 2

▲

All the information in the table on the left is contained in the more compact table on the right.

Column 5 gives the labels for the final statement, just as in the preceding table. This simplified form is recommended once the basic ideas involved in the construction of the table are well understood.

In a table for statements involving three simple statements, eight rows would be needed. In general, if k simple statements are involved, the truth table will contain 2^k rows.

EXERCISES

1. Given p: $2 = 1 + 3$, q: $2 > 3$, and r: $3 > 0$. Translate the following into words:

(a) $\sim p$.   (b) $p \lor q$.   (c) $p \land r$.

(d) $(\sim p) \veebar q$.   (e) $(\sim q) \land r$.   (f) $\sim (p \land r)$.

2. Determine the truth or falsity of the statements in Exercise 1.

3. Construct a truth table for each of the following statements.

(a) $\sim (p \lor q)$.   (b) $p \land (\sim p)$.   (c) $\sim (p \lor q) \land p$.

*4. Give a compound statement for $p \veebar q$, using only $\sim$, $\land$, and $\lor$. Check your answer by creating a truth table and comparing it with the table for $\veebar$.

5. What is the negation of each of the following?

(a) Ice is cold.
(b) John is handsome.
(c) All Russians are Communists.
(d) $2 + 7 = 8$.
(e) There are 30 days in September.

6. Write in words the conjunction and the disjunction of the following:

(a) $6 \cdot 3 = 18$. $3 + 4 = 6$.
(b) The sun is shining. It is raining.
(c) Mary is 8 years old. Sugar is sweet.
(d) Math is easy. Studying is fun.
(e) $2 + 3 > 4$. 5 is an odd number.

+7. For each of the following, construct one truth table containing the two given statements. Check that the columns containing the two given statements are identical. Such statements are said to be *logically equivalent*.

(a) $\sim (\sim p)$; p.
(b) $\sim (p \land q)$; $(\sim p) \lor (\sim q)$.
(c) $\sim (p \lor q)$; $(\sim p) \land (\sim q)$.

(The preceding results give statements which are logically equivalent to the negations of $\sim p$, $p \land q$, and $p \lor q$.)

8. Write the following statements, using logical symbols. Then write the negation of each statement in good English, using the results in Exercise 7 above.

    (a) I am poor and happy.
    (b) Mary or Alice is wrong.
    (c) Chemistry and physics are natural sciences.
    (d) 2 and 13 are prime numbers.
    (e) 127 is prime or composite.
    (f) n or $n + 1$ is even.

9. Let p be "John passed the test" and q be "Jim passed the test." Write in symbolic form the statement, "It is not the case that neither John nor Jim passed the test." Under what circumstances is this statement true?

*10. Write in good English (do not use "It is not the case that . . .") the negation of:

    (a) Some squirrels fly.
    (b) No women are color-blind.
    (c) Some people work hard or all starve.
    (d) For all real numbers x, x^2 is positive.

2–2 CONDITIONAL STATEMENTS

Perhaps the most important kind of compound statement for mathematics is the conditional statement. This kind of statement usually takes the form, "If p, then q." In mathematical statements which have this form, p is called the *hypothesis* and q the *conclusion*. (In logic p is usually called the *antecedent* and q the *consequent*.) A mathematical example is, "If triangle ABC is equilateral, triangle ABC is isosceles." Another way of writing the conditional "If p, then q," is $p \rightarrow q$, read "p implies q."

One of the characteristic features of mathematics is the tendency to extend or "generalize" previous results. In attaching labels true or false to the conditional statement, "If p, then q," we would like to have the table conform to the labels which we would ordinarily assign in cases where common sense would indicate whether the statement was true or false. However, in addition, we would like to tag the sentence with a label in all cases. Let us consider an example. Roger tells Catherine, "If it doesn't rain this afternoon, I will take you for a drive in my convertible." Under what circumstances would Catherine think Roger a prevaricator? If it doesn't rain and Roger never shows up, Catherine would certainly be justified in feeling that Roger had broken his word. However, suppose that it does rain. Whether or not the ride takes place, Catherine would not be justified in saying that Roger had lied to her. Since it would not be reasonable to say that Roger's statement was false, it ought to bear the label *true*.

Since we wish to attach a label to every compound statement, we make the convention that when the hypothesis of a conditional statement is false, we shall tag the statement true. This agrees with the example just given, and in any case does no harm, since as a practical matter the statement is never invoked unless the hypothesis is satisfied. Hence we postulate the following truth table for the conditional statement, "If p, then q."

p	q	$p \rightarrow q$
T	T	T
T	F	F
F	T	T
F	F	T

A conditional statement is false only if the hypothesis is true and the conclusion is false.

Another strange result of our tagging process is that conditionals, as well as disjunctions, involving statements which are not related at all will now bear tags true and false.

EXAMPLE 2–2.1. If John loves Mary, then $2 + 2 = 5$.

This statement is labeled true if John does not love Mary but false if John does love her. Of course, in significant mathematical statements such oddities do not arise because we are usually interested in theorems stated in the form, "If p, then q," only when the two components are related.

In mathematical usage there are several ways of writing conditional statements, all of which mean the same thing. Here is a partial list:

> If p, then q.
> p implies q.
> q is implied by p.
> p only if q.
> p is a sufficient condition for q.
> q is a necessary condition for p.

If we wish to assert that $p \rightarrow q$ and $q \rightarrow p$, we write $p \leftrightarrow q$. The statement $p \leftrightarrow q$, which is called a *biconditional statement*, is logically the same as $(p \rightarrow q) \wedge (q \rightarrow p)$, and is read "$p$ if and only if q." This phrase is used very often in definitions, and in theorems which characterize some set or object.

EXAMPLE 2-2.2

Definition. A triangle is equilateral if and only if all three of its sides are of equal length.

Theorem
A triangle is isosceles if and only if two of its angles are equal.

If we are given a statement $p \rightarrow q$, then $q \rightarrow p$ is called the *converse* of the statement. One of the common logical fallacies is to assume that the converse of any true theorem is true.

EXAMPLE 2-2.3.
If two triangles are congruent, they are similar. (True) Converse: If two triangles are similar, they are congruent. (False)

Another closely related statement is the *contrapositive* of a conditional statement. Given $p \rightarrow q$, the contrapositive is $\sim q \rightarrow \sim p$.

It is sometimes the case that a compound statement has the truth value T for all possible truth values of its component statements, e.g., the statement $p \vee \sim p$ discussed in Section 2-1. Such a statement is called a *tautology*. An especially important example of a *tautology* is given by the following theorem.

Theorem 2-2.1

$(p \rightarrow q) \leftrightarrow (\sim q \rightarrow \sim p)$ *is a tautology.*

Proof. We prove the theorem by constructing a truth table and observing that in all cases the statement has the truth value T. Let r be $(p \rightarrow q)$, and s be $(\sim q \rightarrow \sim p)$. Then to say that $(p \rightarrow q) \leftrightarrow (\sim q \rightarrow \sim p)$ means

$$[(p \rightarrow q) \rightarrow (\sim q \rightarrow \sim p)] \wedge [(\sim q \rightarrow \sim p) \rightarrow (p \rightarrow q)],$$

that is,

$$(r \rightarrow s) \wedge (s \rightarrow r).$$

p	q	r $p \to q$	s $\sim q \to \sim p$	$r \to s$	$s \to r$	$(r \to s) \land (s \to r)$ $(p \to q) \leftrightarrow (\sim q \to \sim p)$
T	T	T	$F\ T\ F$	T	T	T
T	F	F	$T\ F\ F$	T	T	T
F	T	T	$F\ T\ T$	T	T	T
F	F	T	$T\ T\ T$	T	T	T
1	2	3	4 6 5	7	8	9

▲

The preceding truth table also shows that a conditional statement and its contrapositive are *logically equivalent* (see Exercise 7, Section 2–1); that is, the entries in columns 3 and 6 are identical. In fact, we may note that two statements r and s are logically equivalent just in case the biconditional $r \leftrightarrow s$ is a tautology.

Although conditional statements occur very frequently in many parts of mathematics—so much so that we think of mathematics as an "If . . . , then . . ." activity—we could get along with a logically equivalent statement which involves only the connectives not and or, as the following theorem shows.

Theorem 2–2.2

$(p \to q) \leftrightarrow (\sim p \lor q)$ *is a tautology.*

Proof

p	q	$(p \to q) \leftrightarrow (\sim p \lor q)$
T	T	$T\ T\ T\quad T\quad F\ T\ T$
T	F	$T\ F\ F\quad T\quad F\ F\ F$
F	T	$F\ T\ T\quad T\quad T\ T\ T$
F	F	$F\ T\ F\quad T\quad T\ T\ F$
1	2	1 4 2 6 3 5 2

Theorem 2–2.3

$\sim(p \rightarrow q) \leftrightarrow (p \wedge \sim q)$ *is a tautology.*

Proof. See Exercise 5 below.

EXERCISES

1. Translate the following sentences into symbolic statements, using the connectives $\sim$, $\vee$, $\wedge$, $\rightarrow$, $\leftrightarrow$ and letters to stand for the simple statements.

(a) If 5 is an even integer, 15 is divisible by 6.

(b) If Galileo was born before Descartes, then Newton was not born before Shakespeare.

(c) If New York City is north of St. Louis, then the population of Chicago is larger than that of New York City.

(d) If Napoleon was a contemporary of Beethoven and Beethoven was a contemporary of Gauss, then Napoleon and Gauss were contemporaries.

(e) The man in the moon isn't real, and if the same is true of Santa Claus, lots of kiddies are deceived.

Which of these compound statements are true?

2. State the converse and the contrapositive of each of the following:

(a) If a triangle is isosceles, it is equilateral.

(b) If a number is prime and greater than 2, it is odd.

(c) There are no even perfect numbers. [*Hint:* First write the sentence in the form "If p, then q."]

(d) If Jack goes to college, he is more than 12 years old.

(e) I say what I mean. [See the hint for (c).]

3. Construct truth tables for each of the following:

(a) $(p \rightarrow p) \vee (p \rightarrow \sim p)$.

(b) $(p \wedge q) \rightarrow p$.

(c) $(q \rightarrow p) \leftrightarrow (\sim q \vee p)$.

4. Construct a truth table for each of the following, and use it to decide whether or not the statement is a tautology:

(a) $p \leftrightarrow q$.

(b) $p \leftrightarrow (p \vee q)$.

(c) $(p \rightarrow q) \leftrightarrow (q \rightarrow p)$.

(d) $p \rightarrow (\sim p \rightarrow q)$.

(e) $\sim(\sim p) \leftrightarrow p$.

(f) $(p \rightarrow q) \rightarrow [p \rightarrow (p \wedge q)]$.

(g) $\sim(p \wedge q) \leftrightarrow (\sim p \vee \sim q)$.

(h) $[(p \rightarrow q) \wedge \sim p] \rightarrow \sim q$.

(i) $[p \vee (\sim p \vee q)] \vee (\sim p \wedge \sim q)$.

+5. Show that the negation of $p \rightarrow q$ is $p \wedge \sim q$; that is, show by truth tables that $\sim(p \rightarrow q) \leftrightarrow (p \wedge \sim q)$ is a tautology.

$^+$6. The statement $\sim p \rightarrow \sim q$ is called the *inverse* of $p \rightarrow q$. Write a truth table for the inverse of $p \rightarrow q$. Is the inverse logically equivalent to the contrapositive? to the converse?

7. Write the converse, inverse, and contrapositive of each of the following:

(a) $q \rightarrow p$.   (b) $\sim p \rightarrow \sim q$.   (c) $\sim q \rightarrow p$.
(d) $p \rightarrow \sim q$.   (e) $\sim q \rightarrow \sim p$.

$^+$8. $p \rightarrow q$ is often read "*p* is a *sufficient* condition for *q*" or "*q* is a *necessary* condition for *p*." In each of the following, which is the necessary and which is the sufficient condition?

(a) Two lines are parallel if they are equidistant.
(b) $3x^2 + 1 = 4$, only if $x = 1$.
(c) If a number greater than 2 is prime, it is odd.
(d) I will pass this course only if I do my homework regularly.
(e) If it rains, the game will be canceled.

9. Give an example of two statements p and q such that p is necessary, but not sufficient, for q.

10. Give an example of two statements p and q such that p is sufficient, but not necessary, for q.

11. Prove that the negation of "p is a necessary and sufficient condition for q" is logically equivalent to "p is a necessary and sufficient condition for $\sim q$."

12. Is it true that a statement which implies a true statement must be true?

2–3 AXIOMS, DEFINITIONS, AND THEOREMS

We have introduced the basic ideas about sets and mathematical logic which we shall use throughout the book. The claim has been made for mathematics that it is the best and most precise language known for the statement of complicated ideas. We would like now to examine the structure of this language and analyze the rather extravagant claims we have made for it.

One of the bases for the claim to precision is that careful definitions are made for most of the words used in mathematics. For example, in geometry a set of points is *collinear* if and only if there is a line which contains all the points of the set, or a set S is called *convex* if for every two points P and Q belonging to S, the entire segment $\overline{PQ}$ lies in S. However, you will note that these definitions for collinearity and convexity are given in terms of other words which are assumed to be known, in this case "set," "point," "line," "belongs to," and "segment." Some of these may have been defined previously. If so, they must have been defined in terms of other words. If you have ever tried to look up an unfamiliar word in the dictionary, you will grasp the idea. A dictionary is helpful only if you already know a good many words. The same is true in mathematics. "Collinear" is made clear by the definition given above if you already understand what "set," "point," "line," and "contains" mean. Where, then, is our precise language? One of the differences between mathematics and other disciplines is that in mathematics we state clearly at the beginning that we realize it is impossible to define every term. Consequently, we state which terms we shall not try to define. These terms are called, reasonably enough, undefined terms. This does not mean that we are operating completely in the dark. We talk about how these undefined terms will be used, and we try to explain what we assume concerning their properties, but we recognize their logical status at the outset. This is what Bertrand Russell meant by, "... mathematics is the subject in which we never know what we are talking about."

Once the set of undefined terms has been agreed upon, definitions of other terms are then made in terms of these. We make no pretense that all words will be defined in our mathematical system. By a *mathematical definition, we simply mean an agreement on the way in which certain words or symbols will be used.*

If we stopped here, our language would be pretty useless. The next step is to state precisely what properties of our undefined terms we plan to use in this mathematical structure. These statements about the undefined terms are called *axioms* or *postulates*. Axioms were once said to be "self-evident truths"; however, modern developments in mathematics have shown this description to be at best inadequate and usually meaningless. Instead of claiming that axioms are obviously true, we simply assume that the undefined terms have the properties given by the axioms, and investigate the consequences of these assumptions. This set of undefined terms, together with the set of statements about these terms (axioms of the system), and a special set of statements which give the rules of logic used in developing the structure constitute the basis for the mathematical theory being studied. The theory is then developed by making new definitions and proving statements (called theorems) which are logical consequences of the axioms of the system.

Hence when we say that a theorem in a mathematical system is true, we are not making a claim about the physical world or about any absolute standard of truth, but simply that it is a consequence of the axioms and rules of logic which are the basis for the theory. That is, we claim only "If . . . , then. . . ." This is perhaps the most characteristic feature of mathematics. In this light it would appear that mathematics is one of the few pure creations of the mind of men. It is here that the mathematician likes to think that he has an advantage over the physical scientist: he is not essentially dependent on or restricted by the physical world. The mathematician's creativity is limited only by his own imagination and resourcefulness. This freedom to create new systems is usually accompanied by the desire to know the consequences of a set of interesting assumptions. This desire, in turn, at least historically, has usually been prompted by questions which arise concerning situations occurring in the physical world. What, then, is the connection between mathematics and the physical world?

The answer is found in the area of activity usually called applied mathematics. Today this is seen as constructing "mathematical models" which approximate actual physical situations. For example, in that most familiar of mathematical models, Euclidean geometry, the undefined terms, point and line, are frequently suggested by a dot on the blackboard and a series of chalk marks which we call a straight line.

The axioms then state properties of these dots and collections of chalk marks which seem to fit the physical situation being observed:

"Two points determine a line."

"Two lines meet in a point," etc.

From these axioms and rules of logic, such as

$$[(p \rightarrow q) \land (q \rightarrow r)] \rightarrow (p \rightarrow r),$$

and new definitions, the mathematical system of Euclidean geometry develops.

There are two important aspects of this whole procedure which must be noted. (1) The mathematical system contains conclusions which follow from the axioms, definitions, and rules of logic. (2) Wherever a physical situation can be found in which the undefined terms can be suitably interpreted and in which the assumptions about these terms (the axioms) seem to be justified on the basis of observation, then the conclusions (theorems) may be interpreted and tested. If the mathematical model offers a sufficiently accurate picture of the physical situation, then the conclusions are interpreted and used.

This procedure is the basis for all applications of mathematics. Frequently no distinction is made between mathematics and its applications, and this confusion leads to all sorts of misunderstandings about mathematics and its role in the modern world.

Mathematics, then, can furnish a clear and precise language for describing various complicated situations which occur in the world. The usefulness of the resulting mathematical theory, however, is entirely dependent on the appropriateness of the mathematical model which was designed to describe the situation in the first place.

After we have had more experience with various parts of mathematics, we shall take another look at the structure of mathematical systems.

EXERCISES

1. Look up the following words in an unabridged dictionary and try to find a definition for the terms used in a mathematical sense:

(a) set,	(b) group,	(c) equivalent,
(d) equal,	(e) isomorphism,	(f) congruent.

2. Look up the same list of words in the *Mathematics Dictionary* by G. James and R. C. James.

3. Assume that polygon, side, angle, length, equal, and parallel have previously been defined and then define:

(a) triangle,	(b) rhombus,	(c) trapezoid,
(d) parallelogram,	(e) square,	(f) similar triangles,
(g) equilateral triangle,	(h) right angle,	(i) scalene triangle.

4. Criticize the following definitions of terms used in plane geometry. (Assume that point, line, and line segment are undefined terms.) If the definition is poor, devise a better one.

(a) *Intersect:* two lines are said to intersect if they have one or more points in common.

(b) *Parallel:* two lines are said to be parallel if they do not intersect.

(c) *Circle:* the set of points, each of which is at a distance one inch from a given fixed point called the center.

(d) *Congruent:* two geometric figures are said to be congruent if the area of one is equal to the area of the other.

5. Can there be different applications of the same mathematical theory? Give an example, if you can.

6. What is the distinction between an axiom and a theorem in a mathematical system?

2–4 RULES OF INFERENCE AND MATHEMATICAL PROOF

Since mathematics is primarily an "If . . . , then . . ." activity, we shall now take a closer look at the way in which mathematical theorems are proved. We have already mentioned that we are not concerned so much with the "truth" of a mathematical theorem in any absolute sense as with whether it is deducible by a *valid argument* from the axioms and definitions of the system, the rules of logic, and previously deduced theorems.

By an *argument* we mean a set of statements in which the final statement (the *conclusion*) is said to *follow* from an initial statement or set of statements. Such initial statements are called *premises*. If, whenever the premises are all true, it follows that the conclusion must also be true, the argument is a *valid argument*.

Hence, if the premises are true and the conclusion is false, the argument cannot be valid. It is worth noting that an argument may be a valid one without in any way implying that the conclusion of the argument is a true statement. In fact, the truth of the conclusion is neither necessary nor sufficient for the validity of the argument.

EXAMPLE 2–4.1

Premises: All musicians have long hair.
Louis Armstrong is a musician.
Conclusion: Louis Armstrong has long hair.

In this example the argument is *valid;* however, the conclusion is *false*. This is only possible if at least one of the premises fails to be true. In this case the first premise is false and the second one is true.

EXAMPLE 2–4.2

Premises: Some operas by Menotti are melodramatic.
The Consul is an opera by Menotti.
Conclusion: The Consul is melodramatic.

In this case both the premises and the conclusion are *true;* however, the argument is *invalid*. The conclusion, while true, does not follow from the premises.

When we speak of a proof of a mathematical theorem, we mean a valid argument which leads from the premises, which are the axioms of the mathematical system together with the hypothesis of the theorem, to the conclusion of the theorem. The real difficulty in constructing proofs lies in finding a chain of statements which leads to the conclusion of the theorem.

Unfortunately, there is no magic prescription for constructing such a chain of statements. Most good theorems contain a surprise, and the discovery of a valid argument leading to this surprising conclusion often demands considerable ingenuity and at times an original way of looking at the problem. However, the mechanical details involved in ensuring that an argument really is valid are greatly simplified by first obtaining a few additional results from logic.

One of the principal tools in making proofs is the *Rule of Detachment*, sometimes called the rule of *modus ponens*. This *rule of inference* is as follows: If the statement $p \to q$ is true and statement p is true, then statement q is true. This conclusion is based on the axioms for conditional statements contained in the truth table for $p \to q$.

p	q	$p \to q$
T	T	T
T	F	F
F	T	T
F	F	T

Statements p and $p \to q$ are both true only in the first row; in that row q is also true. Hence we can "detach" the truth of the statement q from the truth of $p \to q$ if we know also that p is true. However, note that we cannot conclude that q is true merely from the fact that $p \to q$ is true. (See row 4 of the truth table.)

A second rule of inference is the *Law of the Syllogism*. This asserts that $[(p \to q) \land (q \to r)] \to (p \to r)$. This rule is used to establish that $p \to r$ if $p \to q$ and $q \to r$ have been previously established.

The justification for this rule of inference is the fact that the statement is a tautology. (See Exercise 2 below.)

If we reformulate the Rule of Detachment as $[(p \to q) \land p] \to q$, it also is a tautology. (See Exercise 1 below.)

These two rules of inference, together with a *replacement rule*, which allows any statement in a proof to be replaced by a logically equivalent statement, form the logical basis for most mathematical proofs.

The actual form which the proof takes usually varies with the audience for which the argument is intended. In most cases, a *formal proof* proceeding from a set of premises making repeated use of the Rule of Detachment and the Law of the Syllogism to arrive at the conclusion is too complicated and lengthy.

Mathematical proofs are usually informal, the common practice being to state the important steps in the proof and to rely on the reader to supply missing details. However, mathematicians always work under the assumption that, if pressed, they should be able to furnish a formal proof.

EXERCISES

1. Construct a truth table to show that the Rule of Detachment, $[(p \rightarrow q \wedge p] \rightarrow q$, is a tautology.

2. Show that the Law of the Syllogism,
$$[(p \rightarrow q) \wedge (q \rightarrow r)] \rightarrow (p \rightarrow r),$$
is a tautology.

+3. Construct a truth table to show that $[(p \rightarrow q) \wedge \sim q] \rightarrow \sim p$ is a tautology (*modus tollens*).

4. Construct a truth table to show that $(p \rightarrow q) \leftrightarrow \sim(p \wedge \sim q)$ is a tautology.

+5. A statement which is false for all values of its component statements is called a *contradictory statement*, or a *contradiction*. Show that $p \wedge \sim p$ is a contradictory statement.

6. Which of the following statements are contradictions:

(a) $p \rightarrow \sim p$,

(b) $[(p \rightarrow q) \wedge p] \wedge \sim q$,

(c) $(p \wedge \sim q) \rightarrow (q \rightarrow p)$,

(d) $(p \rightarrow q) \leftrightarrow (p \wedge \sim q)$.

2–5 METHODS OF PROOF

In the last section, we briefly discussed formal and informal proofs. We said that most proofs are informal. However, when this is granted, there are several methods of proof which employ different aspects of the logical machinery which we have developed in this chapter. We will now consider briefly some of these methods.

(1) The direct proof

In a *direct proof* of a theorem which is stated in the form of a conditional statement, the hypothesis is accepted as having the label true without any attempt at justification. The object of the argument is then to deduce the conclusion by a chain of statements, each in turn having the label true. The last step in the proof will then be the assertion that the conclusion also bears this label. In a formal proof a reason is given for asserting that each of the statements is true. Reasons may be definitions, axioms, rules of inference, previous steps in the proof, or previously proved theorems.

Note that in such an argument the conclusion is shown to be true under the assumption that the hypothesis is true. Hence the proof merely shows that if the hypothesis is accepted as true, then the conclusion must be also.

EXAMPLE 2–5.1. If the two integers a and b are even, then their sum, $a + b$, is even.

Proof

STATEMENT	REASON
1. $a = 2a' \quad b = 2b'$.	1. Hypothesis and definition of even (An integer is even if it is divisible by 2.)
2. $a + b = 2a' + 2b'$.	2. Step 1 and the meaning of $=$†
3. $a + b = 2(a' + b') = 2c$.	3. Factoring
4. $a + b$ is even.	4. Step 3 and the definition of even

Notice that we have *not* proved that $a + b$ is even; we have simply proved "*If a* and *b* are even, *then a + b* is even."

The following chain of statements is an example of one way in which the informal argument above can be made more formal.

STATEMENT	REASON
1. p $\quad$ a and b are even.	Hypothesis
2. $p \rightarrow q$ If a and b are even, then $a = 2a'$ and $b = 2b'$.	Definition of even
3. $q \rightarrow r$ If $a = 2a'$ and $b = 2b'$, then $a + b = 2a' + 2b'$.	Meaning of $=$

---

† The symbol $=$, as in the case of sets, is used to indicate that the symbols appearing on either side are names for the same object.

4. $p \rightarrow r$ If a and b are even, then   2 and 3 and the Law
            $a + b = 2a' + 2b'$.   of the Syllogism

5. $r \rightarrow s$ If $a + b = 2a' + 2b'$, then   Factoring
            $a + b = 2(a' + b') = 2c$.

6. $p \rightarrow s$ If a and b are even, then   4 and 5 and the Law
            $a + b = 2c$.   of the Syllogism

7. $s \rightarrow t$ If $a + b = 2c$, then $a + b$ Definition of even
            is even.

8. $p \rightarrow t$ If a and b are even, then   6 and 7 and the Law
            $a + b$ is even.   of the Syllogism

9. t $a + b$ is even.   1 and 8 and the Rule
                                    of Detachment

If we had chosen to make the theorem itself the final statement of the proof, notice that we could simply leave off steps 1 and 9.

We can see that the formal argument actually contains no new ideas, only the additional logic which carries the argument. Such proofs are rarely given in mathematics, but it is well to note that this logical machinery is always in the background of a valid proof and could be supplied if desired.

(2) Indirect proof

Indirect proofs are based on the use of logically equivalent statements of the theorem. For example, since $(p \rightarrow q) \leftrightarrow (\sim q \rightarrow \sim p)$, if we show that $\sim q \rightarrow \sim p$, then we have proved that $p \rightarrow q$, since for any combination of truth values for the component statements p and q, the conditional and its contrapositive have the same truth values.

EXAMPLE 2-5.2. If n^2 is even, then n is even. $(p \rightarrow q)$

We prove this theorem indirectly by proving its contrapositive $\sim q \rightarrow \sim p$; that is, we shall prove: If n is not even, then n^2 is not even. This is the same as saying: If n is odd, then n^2 is odd.

Proof

STATEMENT   REASON

1. $n = 2m + 1$ 1. Definition of an odd integer. (An integer is odd if it is not divisible by 2; that is, its remainder is 1 when dividing by 2.)

2. $n^2 = (2m + 1)^2$ 2. Meaning of $=$
   $\qquad = 4m^2 + 4m + 1$ Simplifying, using axioms
   $\qquad = 2(2m^2 + 2m) + 1$ from algebra
   $\qquad = 2M + 1.$

3. n^2 is odd.   3. Step 2 and the definition of
                                            an odd integer

Since we have proved that $\sim q \rightarrow \sim p$, which is logically equivalent to $p \rightarrow q$ (that is, they have the same truth values), we have proved the original theorem.

A second indirect method of proof is called *reductio ad absurdum*, or "proof by contradiction." In this method we show that $p \rightarrow q$ is true by showing that its negation $\sim(p \rightarrow q)$ is false. We showed in Exercise 5 of the exercises in Section 2–2 that $\sim(p \rightarrow q) \leftrightarrow (p \wedge \sim q)$. Hence we need to show that $p \wedge \sim q$ is false. This is usually accomplished by proving that $(p \wedge \sim q) \rightarrow (r \wedge \sim r)$. However, in Exercise 5 of the exercises in Section 2–4, we showed that $r \wedge \sim r$ is a contradiction, i.e., a statement which is always false. Since $r \wedge \sim r$ is always false, $(p \wedge \sim q) \rightarrow (r \wedge \sim r)$ can hold only if $p \wedge \sim q$ is false, i.e., if $\sim(p \rightarrow q)$ is false or $p \rightarrow q$ is true.

Thus we see that the proof of $p \rightarrow q$ by contradiction essentially consists of assuming that $p \wedge \sim q$, the conjunction of the hypothesis and the negation of the conclusion, is true and reaching a contradiction. Again the logical justification usually remains in the background, but it is always available to justify a more informal proof. We give as an example Euclid's celebrated proof that there are infinitely many prime numbers.

Definition 2–5.1. A *prime number* is an integer greater than 1 which has no positive divisors except itself and 1.

EXAMPLE 2–5.3

If $S = \{x \mid x \text{ is prime}\}$, S is not finite. $(p \rightarrow q)$

We prove the theorem using *reductio ad absurdum*.
Suppose that the set of primes is finite; that is,

$$S = \{p_1, p_2, \ldots, p_k\}.\dagger$$

---

† The numbers attached to the p's and written slightly below the line are called *subscripts*. They are used to distinguish one prime from another.

STATEMENT		REASON
1. $p \wedge \sim q$ $S = \{p_1, p_2, \ldots, p_k\}$.		Hypotheses and definition of finite set
2.	Let $n = p_1 p_2 p_3 \ldots p_k + 1$.	Definition of n
3. r	Let π be a prime which divides n.	Every integer greater than 1 is divisible by a prime.
4.	$\pi = p_i$ for some $i = 1, 2, \ldots, k$.	Every prime is in S, the set of all primes by step 1.
5. $\sim r$	π does not divide n.	Since $\pi = p_i$ for some i, n/π has remainder 1.
6. $r \wedge \sim r$	Contradiction: π divides n and π does not divide n.	Steps 3 and 5

Since $p \wedge \sim q$ leads to a contradiction, $r \wedge \sim r$, we have established $p \rightarrow q$.

We have discussed briefly direct and indirect methods of proof which are often employed. However, from time to time a statement which we try to prove may turn out to be false. This knowledge is sometimes as useful as knowing that a theorem is true. Consider the statement, "For all integers x, $x^2 + x + 41$ is prime." To disprove this statement, we first write it in the "If . . . , then . . ." form: If x is an integer, $x^2 + x + 41$ is prime. We need only notice that for $x = 41$,

$$x^2 + x + 41 = 41^2 + 41 + 41 = 41(41 + 1 + 1) = 41 \cdot 43.$$

Since, in this case, $x^2 + x + 41$ has the divisors 41 and 43, in addition to 1 and itself, it is not prime. This exception is called a *counterexample*. Its existence proves that the statement cannot be true for all integers x; consequently, it would have been impossible to prove the statement.

EXERCISES

1. Construct direct proofs for the following theorems:
    (a) If n is an even integer, then n^2 is an even integer.
    (b) The product of an odd integer and an even integer is even.
    (c) The sum of two odd integers is even.
    (d) $(A \subset B \wedge B \subset C) \rightarrow A \subset C$.

(e) If a divides b and b divides c, then a divides $(b + c)$. [*Hint:* a divides b if and only if there is an integer q such that $a \cdot q = b$.]

2. Give an indirect proof of each of the following:
   (a) If n^2 is an odd integer, then n is an odd integer.
   (b) The sum of two odd integers is even.
   (c) $[A \subset B$ and $A \cap B = \emptyset] \rightarrow (A = \emptyset)$.

3. Give counterexamples to disprove each of the following statements:
   (a) If x is a real number, $x^2 > 0$.
   (b) If $a > b$, $1/b > 1/a$.
   (c) If $ca = cb$, then $a = b$.
   (d) If a and b are real numbers, then $a^2 + b^2 > 2ab$.
   (e) If $a > b$, then $a^2 > b^2$.
   (f) If a quadrilateral is a parallelogram, then it is a rectangle.
   (g) Only odd numbers are prime.

4. For each of the following, give a proof if the statement is true; if not, give a counterexample.
   (a) For all real numbers x, $x^2 - 3x = x + 2$.
   (b) For all real numbers x, $x^2 - 9 = (x + 3)(x - 3)$.
   (c) $[(p \lor q) \land \sim q] \rightarrow p$.
   *(d) If $x^2 \geq 0$ for all x, then $a^2 + b^2 \geq 2ab$.

*2–6 QUANTIFIED STATEMENTS

At several places in this chapter, we have encountered phrases such as "For all integers, . . . ," "Some men are . . . ," "All men are. . . ." When a statement contains phrases such as these, the statement is said to be *quantified*. In stating the negation of a simple statement, and especially in stating the contrapositive and the negation of a conditional statement, the presence of such phrases leads to much confusion in ordinary discourse. Any serious treatment of logic must take into account these difficulties and establish methods for dealing with them.

The important point which must somehow be accommodated is that if p is a true statement, not-p has to be false and vice versa. For example, if p is "All men are bald" (a false statement), its negation, $\sim p$, must be true. If one attempts to ignore the quantifier all and simply negates the verb are, the resulting statement "All men are not bald" is equally false. It cannot then be the negation of the original statement. We achieved the negation of the statement in Section 2–1 by placing *not* in front of the entire statement. The statement then becomes "Not all men are bald." If we think about this for a moment, we see that what we are actually saying is that there is at least one man who is not bald; i.e., "Some (meaning at least one) men are not bald." We may then check that the negation of this false statement is indeed true, as it should be according to our axioms.

The word "all" or the phrase "for all..." is a so-called *universal quantifier*. The assertion is that every member of some class has a certain property. On the other hand, "some" or "there exists a..." is called an *existential quantifier* and the assertion is that at least one member of a certain class possesses the property in question (maybe more than one, possibly even all members).

A satisfactory treatment of this matter would necessitate a discussion of such matters as variables, open sentences, and the like. These notions will be treated in Chapter 4. For our purposes the following rule-of-thumb will be sufficient for simple statements: The negation of a statement "All... are ..." is "Some... are not ..." or "Not all... are ... ." Similarly, the negation of "Some... are ..." is "All... are not ... ."

EXAMPLE 2–6.1.

Statement: All girls are pretty.
Negation: Some girls are not pretty.
            Or
            Not all girls are pretty.

EXAMPLE 2–6.2.

Statement: There is at least one intelligent person in Congress.
Negation: No congressmen are intelligent.

In mathematics, as in other areas, quantifiers are not specifically stated in most instances. They are assumed to be understood from the context. However, this practice often leads to confusion and misunderstanding.

As an example of the use of quantifiers in mathematics, the finding of a counterexample to show that a statement is false presumes that the universal quantifier was understood to apply to the original statement: "For all integers x, $x^2 + x + 41$ is prime." The negation of this statement is "There is an integer x for which $x^2 + x + 41$ is not prime." Since this last statement is true (let $x = 41$), the original statement is false.

The negation of quantified compound statements is somewhat more complicated. We recall (Exercise 7, Section 2–1 and Exercise 5, Section 2–2) that the negation of

$$p \wedge q \quad \text{is} \quad \sim p \vee \sim q;$$

$$\sim(p \vee q) \leftrightarrow \sim p \wedge \sim q;$$

$$\sim(p \rightarrow q) \leftrightarrow (p \wedge \sim q).$$

The rule-of-thumb that we change universal quantifiers to existential quantifiers and negate the predicate, or change the existential quantifier to the universal quantifier and negate the predicate, still holds. However, care must be taken to distinguish cases in which the entire compound statement is quantified from those in which only one of the component parts is affected by the quantifier.

EXAMPLE 2–6.3.

Statement: All Capitalist countries are wealthy and some Socialist countries are not poor.

Negation: Some Capitalist countries are not wealthy or all Socialist countries are poor.

EXAMPLE 2–6.4.

Statement: Some smokers do not get cancer or all smokers are shortening their lives.

Negation: All smokers get cancer and some smokers are not shortening their lives.

EXAMPLE 2–6.5.

Statement: For any pair of triangles, if corresponding angles are equal, the triangles are similar.

Negation: There is a pair of triangles in which the corresponding angles are equal and the triangles are not similar.

The symbols frequently used to denote the universal and the existential quantifiers are ∀ and ∃ [upside down A (all) and backwards E (there exists)], respectively.

EXERCISES

1. Form the negation of each of the following statements:
   - (a) Every integer is a rational number.
   - (b) Some men are fathers.
   - (c) Not every member of the American Civil Liberties Union is a Socialist.
   - (d) Some athletes are not good students.
   - (e) For all integers x, $x > 1$.

2. For each of the parts in the exercise above, decide whether the given statement is true or false and check that the negation has the opposite truth value.

3. Supply any implied quantifiers and form the negation of each of the following statements:
   - (a) Animals are carnivorous and birds are vegetarians.
   - (b) People are mean and God is loving.
   - (c) The writings of philosophers are either ambiguous or unintelligible.
   - (d) All Christians are sinners or some of them are hypocritical.
   - (e) Either the square of a real number is positive or the number is zero.

4. Write the negation of each of the following:
   - (a) $\forall p \, (p \wedge q \rightarrow p)$.
   - (b) $\forall p \, (p \wedge \sim p)$ is false.
   - (c) $\exists p$ such that $(\sim p \wedge p)$ is true.
   - (d) $\forall A \, \exists B$ such that $A \cap B = B$.
   - (e) $\forall A \, \forall B$, $A \cup B = U$.

REVIEW EXERCISES

1. Suppose we know that p is true and q is false. Determine the truth value of:
   - (a) $\sim(p \vee \sim q)$.
   - (b) $p \rightarrow q$.
   - (c) $\sim p \rightarrow \sim q$.
   - (d) $\sim(\sim p) \wedge \sim q$.
   - (e) $p \leftrightarrow q$.

2. Given that A and B are true statements and C and D are false statements, find the truth values of:
   - (a) $\sim(A \wedge C)$.
   - (b) $(A \vee C) \wedge (B \wedge \sim D)$.
   - (c) $\sim[\sim A \vee (\sim C \vee D)]$.
   - (d) $(\sim C \wedge A) \rightarrow [(B \vee D) \vee C]$.
   - (e) $\{\sim B \vee [\sim(C \vee A) \rightarrow D]\} \leftrightarrow [\sim(B \wedge D) \vee C]$.

3. Write the converse of the statement, "If the Communists approve of a man, he follows the party line." Rewrite the original statement, using the phrase, "is a necessary condition."

4. Is $(p \land q) \to (p \lor q)$ a tautology? Justify your answer.

5. A man promised his girl, "I will marry you only if I get a raise." He got his raise and subsequently married a different girl. If the first girl sues for breach of promise, should she logically win her suit?

6. For what truth values for p and q is $[(p \to q) \land \sim p] \to \sim q$ a true statement?

7. Prove that if A and B are disjoint, $B \subset \overline{A}$.

8. Describe the logical argument for a "proof by contradiction."

9. How do the following differ? An axiom, a definition, and a theorem.

Suggested Readings

EVENSON, A. B., *Modern Mathematics*, Scott, Foresman and Co., Chicago, 1962, Ch. 7, pp. 141–164.

FUJII, J. N., *An Introduction to the Elements of Mathematics*, John Wiley, New York, 1961, Ch. 3 and 4, pp. 24–59.

JONES, B. W., *Elementary Concepts of Mathematics*, second edition, Macmillan, New York, 1963, Ch. 2, pp. 12–43.

General References

ALLENDOERFER, C. B. and C. O. OAKLEY, *Principles of Mathematics*, second edition, McGraw-Hill, New York, 1963, Ch. 1, pp. 1–47.

EXNER, R. M. and M. F. ROSSKOPF, *Logic in Elementary Mathematics*, McGraw-Hill, New York, 1959.

FÉLIX, L., *The Modern Aspect of Mathematics*, Basic Books, New York, 1960.

KEMENY, J. G., J. L. SNELL, and G. L. THOMPSON, *Introduction to Finite Mathematics*, Prentice-Hall, Englewood Cliffs, N. J., 1957, Ch. 1, pp. 1–53.

NCTM Twenty-third Yearbook, *Insights into Modern Mathematics*, "Deductive Methods in Mathematics" by C. B. Allendoerfer, NCTM, Washington, 1957, pp. 65–99.

RICHARDSON, M., *Fundamentals of Mathematics*, Macmillan, New York, 1958, Ch. 2, pp. 6–40.

STABLER, E. R., *An Introduction to Mathematical Thought*, Addison-Wesley, Reading, Mass., 1953, Ch. 3, pp. 43–75.

SUPPES, P., *Introduction to Logic*, Van Nostrand, Princeton, 1957.

TARSKI, A., "Symbolic Logic" from *The World of Mathematics* edited by J. R. Newman, Simon and Schuster, New York, 1956, Vol. III, pp. 1901–1931.

3 | SETS OF NUMBERS

3-1 THE NATURAL NUMBERS

We have already had occasion to refer to the *natural numbers* many times in Chapter 1. However, aside from a discussion of threeness in Section 1–3, we haven't really tried to define or to explain precisely what a natural number is. There are two reasons for this: First, the natural numbers, or the numbers we count with, are so familiar that everyone feels that he knows about them. Second, to give a precise definition turns out to be a very difficult task, demanding the highest order of technical virtuosity. This instinctive feeling which we all seem to have for the natural numbers is reflected in the remark of the German mathematician Leopold Kronecker, "God created the integers; all else is the work of man." While this number sense—which we indicated in Chapter 1 is really an abstraction from our recognition of the common property of a class of sets—is really one of the oldest parts of civilized man's inheritance, it was not until within the last hundred years that serious attempts were made to give sets of axioms which would "characterize" the set of natural numbers. The set of axioms formulated by G. Peano (1858–1932), while not characterizing the natural numbers in the sense that the set of natural numbers and only this set satisfies Peano's axioms, does, when suitably augmented, form a basis for all of arithmetic.

The detailed study and formulation of a satisfactory definition for the natural numbers was carried out in the work of the German logician G. Frege and the English philosophers and mathematicians Alfred North Whitehead and Bertrand Russell.

While we shall not attempt to develop all of arithmetic from Peano's axioms, a brief look at his axioms and some of their consequences may help to illustrate the idea of a mathematical theory which we discussed in Chapter 2.

There are three essentials in counting: something to count with, the idea of "comes after," and a place to begin. These were recognized and became the undefined terms "(natural) number," "successor," and "1" in Peano's system. The properties which these terms were assumed to have were specified in the following axioms:

P_1. 1 is a number.

P_2. If n is any number, then there exists a unique number n' which is the successor of n.

P_3. 1 is not the successor of any number; that is, $1 \neq n'$ for any n.

P_4. No two numbers have the same successor; that is,

$$n' = m' \rightarrow n = m.$$

P_5. If S is any set of numbers which has the properties, (i) $1 \in S$, (ii) $k \in S \rightarrow k' \in S$, then all numbers belong to S.

Since 1 is a number by P_1, it has a successor $1'$ by P_2. Suppose that we define 2 to be the successor of 1. Then by P_2, 2 is a number. It, in turn, has a successor $2'$. We define 3 to be that successor, etc. This process continues indefinitely, since by P_4 we never return to a number previously defined, and by P_3 we never return to 1.

Addition can then be defined as follows:

$$\text{(i) } n + 1 = n'. \qquad \text{(ii) } n + k' = (n + k)'.$$

This *recursive* definition defines any sum $a + b$; for example,

$4 + 2 = 4 + 1'$	Definition of 2
$= (4 + 1)'$	Definition of addition (ii)
$= (4')'$	Definition of addition (i)
$= (5)'$	Definition of 5
$= 6.$	Definition of 6

Multiplication, in turn, can be defined in terms of addition:

$$\text{(i) } n \cdot 1 = n. \qquad \text{(ii) } n \cdot k' = n \cdot k + n.$$

This *recursive* definition defines any product of natural numbers; for example,

$$4 \cdot 3 = 4 \cdot 2' \qquad \text{Definition of 3}$$
$$= 4 \cdot 2 + 4 \qquad \text{Definition of multiplication (ii)}$$
$$= 4 \cdot 1' + 4 \qquad \text{Definition of 2}$$
$$= (4 \cdot 1 + 4) + 4 \quad \text{Definition of multiplication (ii)}$$
$$= (4 + 4) + 4 \qquad \text{Definition of multiplication (i)}$$
$$= 8 + 4 \qquad \text{Addition}$$
$$= 12. \qquad \text{Addition}$$

From these axioms and definitions all the theorems of arithmetic can now be proved.

So far we have said nothing of P_5. It seems like a reasonable axiom, since if we take a set S having properties,

$$\text{(i) } 1 \in S, \qquad \text{(ii) } [n \in S] \rightarrow [n' = (n + 1) \in S],$$

$1 \in S$ by (i); $2 = 1' \in S$ by (ii). Then using (ii) again, $2' = 3$ belongs. And it seems clear that if we ask ourselves whether any particular number, say 311, belongs, we have only to repeat the preceding argument 310 times to be sure that 311 belongs. Clearly, there was nothing special about 311; a similar argument would suffice for any particular number n. The reason we need P_5 as an axiom is simply that saying any particular number belongs is not quite the same as saying all numbers belong. In fact, the effect of P_5 is just to state explicitly that the process of generating successors produces *all* the natural numbers. The axiom P_5 is extremely useful, and we shall return to it again in the next section.

EXERCISES

1. What number is the successor of:

(a) $1'$.   (b) 15.   (c) $5 + 3'$.   (d) $(2 \cdot 5')'$.   (e) $(5 + 2')'$.

2. Given $E = \{x \mid x \text{ is even}\}$, $0 = \{x \mid x \text{ is odd}\}$, and

$$P = \{x \mid x \text{ is prime}\},$$

which of the following sets is the set of all natural numbers? (U is understood to be the set of all natural numbers.)

(a) $P \cup E$.

(b) $(P \cap 0) \cup E$.

(c) $E \cap 0$.

(d) $E \cup 0$.

(e) $\bar{E} \cup P$.

(f) $(\bar{P} \cup 0) \cup \{2\}$.

3. Compute the following, using only Peano's axioms and the definitions for addition and multiplication. (In any particular part of this question, you may use the results from preceding parts.)

　　(a) $2 + 1$.　　　　　　　(b) $3 + 2$.　　　　　　　(c) $4 \cdot 2 + 2$.
　　(d) $5 \cdot 3 + 4 \cdot 2$.　　　(e) $(5 \cdot 2' + 3)'$.

4. By computing each side separately, as in Exercise 3, prove that

　　(a) $2 + 3 = 3 + 2$.　　　　　　(b) $2 \cdot 3 = 3 \cdot 2$.

3–2 MATHEMATICAL INDUCTION

In Section 3–1 we promised to take another look at axiom P_5 for the natural numbers. It furnishes us with still another method of proof which has a very special character and a flavor all its own. This method is extremely useful in proving certain kinds of mathematical statements, in particular theorems which assert that a certain proposition holds for all natural numbers. The following three examples come from three different branches of mathematics, but their proofs are identical in form, depending on Peano's axiom P_5.

> EXAMPLE 3–2.1. If n is a natural number, the sum of the first n natural numbers is $n(n + 1)/2$.

> EXAMPLE 3–2.2. $3^{2n} - 1$ is divisible by 8 for all natural numbers n.

> EXAMPLE 3–2.3. If A is a set containing n elements, then A has exactly 2^n subsets.

In each of these examples, we use the axiom P_5 in the following way. We consider the set S of natural numbers for which the statement is true. We show that (i) $1 \in S$ and (ii) $k \in S \rightarrow (k + 1) \in S$. We then apply axiom P_5 to say that S contains all the natural numbers; that is, the set of natural numbers for which the theorem is true is actually the set of *all* natural numbers.

> *Proof:* Let S be the set of natural numbers for which the theorem is true.

EXAMPLE 3-2.1

Step 1. $1 \in S$

$$1 = \frac{1(1+1)}{2}$$

$$1 = \frac{1 \cdot 2}{2}$$

$$1 = 1$$

Step 2. $k \in S \to (k+1) \in S$

$k \in S$

$$1 + \cdots + k = \frac{k(k+1)}{2}$$

$$1 + \cdots + k + (k+1) = \frac{k(k+1)}{2} + (k+1)$$
$$= (k+1)\left(\frac{k}{2} + 1\right)$$
$$= \frac{(k+1)(k+2)}{2}$$

$(k+1) \in S$

$$1 + \cdots + k + (k+1) = \frac{(k+1)[(k+1)+1]}{2}$$

EXAMPLE 3-2.2

$$3^{2 \cdot 1} - 1 = 3^2 - 1$$
$$= 9 - 1$$
$$= 8$$

$$3^{2k} - 1 = 8q$$

$$3^{2(k+1)} - 1 = 3^{2k+2} - 1$$
$$= 3^{2k} \times 3^2 - 1$$
$$= 3^{2k}(8 + 1) - 1$$
$$= 3^{2k} \times 8 + (3^{2k} - 1)$$
$$= 3^{2k} \times 8 + 8q$$

$$3^{2(k+1)} - 1 = 8(3^{2k} + q)$$

EXAMPLE 3-2.3

Let $A_1 = \{a_1\}$. Then A_1 has $2^1 = 2$ subsets, $\emptyset$ and $\{a_1\}$.

$A_k = \{a_1, a_2, \ldots, a_k\}$ has 2^k subsets.

$A_{k+1} = \{a_1, a_2, \ldots, a_k, a_{k+1}\}$.

The subsets of A_{k+1} are the subsets of A_k (there are 2^k of them) plus those involving a_{k+1}. But from each subset of A_k, there are 2 ways to form a subset of A_{k+1}: by adding a_{k+1} to the subset or not adding it.

Therefore, there are $2 \times 2^k = 2^{k+1}$ ways to form subsets of A_{k+1}.

Step 3. Since the set S of natural numbers for which the theorems are true has the properties, (i) $1 \in S$ by step 1, and (ii) $k \in S \to (k+1) \in S$ by step 2, by P_5, S contains all natural numbers; that is, the theorems are true for all natural numbers n.

EXERCISES

Prove 1–7 by mathematical induction:

1. $2n$ is the nth even integer.

2. $2n - 1$ is the nth odd integer.

3. The sum of the first n odd integers is n^2.

4. $2^{3n} - 1$ is divisible by 7 for all natural numbers n.

⁺5. $1 + r + r^2 + \cdots + r^n = \dfrac{1 - r^{n+1}}{1 - r}, r \neq 1.$

⁺6. $1^2 + 2^2 + \cdots + n^2 = \dfrac{n(n + 1)(2n + 1)}{6}.$

⁺7. $a + (a + d) + \cdots + [a + (n - 1)d] = \dfrac{n[2a + (n - 1)d]}{2}.$

*8. For all $n \geq 4, 2^n < n!$†

*9. In each of the following, try to construct a proof by induction and point out where the attempt fails.

    (a) $2(n + 1) = 2n.$

    (b) $n^2 + 41n + 41$ is prime.

    (c) $1 + 2 + \cdots + n = 5 + \dfrac{n(n + 1)}{2}.$

⁺10. Prove that if T is a set of natural numbers, each element of T being greater than or equal to a natural number t_0, and in addition (i) $t_0 \in T$ and (ii) $k \in T \rightarrow (k + 1) \in T$, then T is the set of all integers greater than or equal to t_0.

3–3 THE INTEGERS

In the last three sections of this chapter, we shall take a brief look at extensions of the system of natural numbers which have been brought about by attempts to solve certain mathematical problems. There are many ways to approach these extended systems of numbers, and we have chosen ways which are convenient because of the machinery of sets and logic which we have at our disposal.

In the section on the natural numbers we remarked that Peano's axioms form an axiomatic basis for arithmetic. We defined addition

---

† The symbol $n!$ stands for the product of the first n natural numbers,

$$n! = 1 \cdot 2 \cdot 3 \ldots n,$$

and is read n factorial.

and multiplication. From these definitions we were able to find a natural number which is the sum or one which is the product of any two given natural numbers. The technical way of putting this is to say that the natural numbers are *closed* under the operations of addition and multiplication. This means that the system of natural numbers contains all numbers which we need in performing the operations of addition and multiplication on any two natural numbers. However, just as natural a question as "What is the sum of 3 and 5?" is the question, "What must be added to 3 to obtain 8?" In essence, what we are seeking is a natural number, call it n, which when added to 3 gives 8; that is, the solution of the equation $3 + n = 8$. The answer is clearly 5. However, what would be the solution to the similar equation $5 + n = 3$? A moment's reflection convinces us that there is no natural number n which, added to 5, gives 3; for 1 is the smallest natural number, and $5 + 1 = 6$. Any larger natural number added to 5 would certainly be more than 6, and therefore could not possibly be 3.

The obvious answer, then, is that there is no solution in the set of natural numbers for this problem. In general, if we pick any two natural numbers a and b and ask what natural number x has the property that $b + x = a$, we are frequently out of luck.

To solve problems of this sort we need a larger system of numbers. In fact, if we were to use the mathematician's prerogative of making new definitions, an obvious choice would be to define numbers which would solve such problems. Before doing this, we make a slight digression to introduce a new notion which will be very useful throughout the rest of this book.

In many parts of mathematics we need the concept of an ordered pair of objects. By an *ordered pair* we simply mean a pair of objects in which we distinguish the first member of the pair from the second. For example, (a, b) denotes the pair of objects a and b in which a is the first member of the pair and b is the second. This pair is different from the pair (b, a), which is made up of the same two elements but taken in a different order.

Now if we return to the problem of devising new numbers to be solutions to equations $b + x = a$, in which a and b are any two natural numbers, we may proceed as follows.

We simply postulate the existence of numbers which satisfy the equation $b + x = a$ for all natural numbers a and b. We attribute to these new numbers properties which we think desirable and necessary. We try to do this in such a way that the new set of numbers will contain a subset which we may identify with the natural numbers and which will have all the properties of the natural numbers, but in addition the new set will contain solutions to equations $b + x = a$, which had no solutions in the set of natural numbers.

We shall call these new numbers *integers*, and as a very temporary symbol for these numbers, we shall use a notation suggested by the problem under consideration. We want solutions for every equation $b + x = a$, where a and b are natural numbers. Accordingly, we denote the solution of any given equation by the ordered pair (a, b) of natural numbers occurring in that equation.

We therefore have symbols for numbers which are solutions to every possible equation of the form $b + x = a$, a and b natural numbers. However, it is clear that not all these symbols stand for different numbers: $2 + x = 3$ $(b + x = a)$ and $3 + x = 4$ $(d + x = c)$ obviously have the same natural number 1 as their solution. Accordingly, we say that two of these numbers (a, b) and (c, d) are "equal" if and only if $a + d = b + c$. This is consistent with the example given above, since $3 + 3 = 2 + 4$. Note also that this usage of equal is consistent with our previous use of the symbol $=$. When we say $(a, b) = (c, d)$, we mean that (a, b) and (c, d) are simply different symbols for the same number.

This procedure has the virtue that it solves our problem of obtaining solutions to all equations of the sort $b + x = a$, where a and b are natural numbers, while using only the concept of an ordered pair of natural numbers and a new definition of equality.

If this procedure seems slightly mysterious, we need only notice that the ordered pair of natural numbers (a, b) is simply a fancy way of writing the difference, $a - b$, of the two natural numbers a and b. If b is less than a, (a, b) stands for the natural number $a - b$, which was the solution to $b + x = a$ in the set of natural numbers. These pairs (a, b) with $b < a$ we identify with the natural numbers $a - b$ which were solutions, present from the beginning. If, however, $b = a$, (a, b) is the new number, *zero*, an integer but not a natural number. Similarly, if a is less than b, (a, b) is something new—a *negative integer* and a solution to the equation $b + x = a$ (a less than b), which had no solution before. Although for a given equation $b + x = a$ (for example, $5 + x = 2$) the solution (a, b), that is, $(2, 5)$ or -3, is unique, there are many equations with -3 as the solution with different a's and b's; for example $8 + x = 5$, $4 + x = 1$, $15 + x = 12$, etc.

This is the reason for the rather strange definition of equality for integers given above.

$$(5, 8) = (1, 4), \qquad \text{since} \qquad 5 + 4 = 8 + 1;$$
$$(5, 8) = (12, 15), \qquad \text{since} \qquad 5 + 15 = 8 + 12;$$
$$(5, 8) = (2, 5), \qquad \text{since} \qquad 5 + 5 = 8 + 2;$$
$$(1, 4) = (12, 15), \qquad \text{since} \qquad 1 + 15 = 4 + 12;$$
$$(1, 4) = (2, 5), \qquad \text{since} \qquad 1 + 5 = 4 + 2;$$
$$(12, 15) = (2, 5), \qquad \text{since} \qquad 12 + 5 = 15 + 2.$$

This way of writing the integers is an interesting example of the kind of dazzling technical virtuosity of the present-day mathematician. With the modest beginnings of Peano's axioms for the natural numbers and the additional notion of ordered pairs of natural numbers, the arithmetic of integers can be developed. Only one additional step in the process will be mentioned. We saw above that the representation of any particular integer was not unique; in fact, there are infinitely many ordered pairs which represent any particular integer. So in order to establish the connection between these elaborate symbols and the familiar notation for integers, we simply agree to denote by a new symbol each integer which previously was represented by any member of an infinite set of ordered pairs of natural numbers, all equal to each other. These symbols are the familiar ones for the integers . . . , $-3, -2, -1$, $0, 1, 2, 3, \ldots$. For example:

The integer represented by any member of

$$\{(x, y) \mid x \text{ and } y \text{ are natural numbers} \wedge (x, y) = (2, 1)\}$$

will be denoted by the symbol 1.

The integer represented by any member of

$$\{(x, y) \mid x \text{ and } y \text{ are natural numbers} \wedge (x, y) = (1, 1)\}$$

will be denoted by 0.

The integer represented by any member of

$$\{(x, y) \mid x \text{ and } y \text{ are natural numbers} \wedge (x, y) = (1, 2)\}$$

will be denoted by -1; etc.

We have only sketched the basic ideas in this construction. In particular, we have not defined addition or multiplication for integers. The details are complicated and cumbersome. However, the point is that from the natural numbers, we have constructed new numbers which can be shown to be solutions to a problem which was frequently unsolvable in the set of natural numbers and which can be shown to have all the properties that integers or whole numbers are supposed to possess.

In addition to obtaining solutions to all equations $b + x = a$, where a and b are natural numbers by this procedure, we get as a bonus solutions to equations of the form $b + x = a$, where a and b are any two *integers*.

We shall not pursue the matter further and *we* certainly *do not intend to use the ordered pair symbol for integers again.* From now on, we will use freely and without reservation the familiar symbols . . . , -3, $-2, -1, 0, 1, 2, 3, . . .$, for the integers and all the properties you have been taught they possess.

To sum up, the preceding discussion was designed to show that we could define a new set of numbers, the integers, which would furnish solutions to equations of the form $b + x = a$, where a and b are any two natural numbers. If b is less than a, the solution is identified with a natural number. If $a = b$, the solution is called zero and is denoted by 0. If b is greater than a, the solution is called a *negative integer*. The natural numbers are then called *positive integers*. The set of *integers* is then the union of three disjoint sets: the set of natural numbers, the set consisting of zero, and the set of negative integers.

The integers may be represented geometrically by taking a line and fixing a point on it. We then identify this point with the integer 0, and select an arbitrary length and mark off points to the right and left of zero. We identify the first such point to the right with the natural number 1, the second with 2, etc., and the ones to the left with $-1, -2$, etc., as in Fig. 3–1.

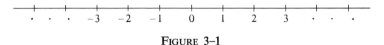

FIGURE 3–1

"Less than," denoted by $<$, (which we have used above, relying only on your intuition) means "to the left of" on this line. For example, $-2 < 1, 3 < 5$, etc.

EXERCISES

1. Which of the following equations have solutions which are natural numbers? Find the solutions.

      (a) $5 + x = 3$.   (b) $6 + x = 7$.   (c) $8 + x = 10$.
      (d) $11 + x = 8$.   (e) $11 + x = 11$.

2. Which equations in Exercise 1 above have solutions which are integers but not natural numbers? Find the solutions to these equations.

3. Draw a Venn diagram showing the sets $P =$ positive integers, $Z = \{0\}$, $N =$ negative integers, $I =$ integers.

4. Give three integers which are not natural numbers.

5. How many natural numbers are less than 5?

6. How many integers are less than 5?

7. Is the set of integers equal to the set of natural numbers? Justify your answer.

*8. Is the set of integers equivalent to the set of natural numbers? Justify your answer.

3-4 THE RATIONAL NUMBERS

In the last section we looked at a method for adding to the set of natural numbers new numbers which would furnish solutions to all equations of the form $b + x = a$, where a and b were any natural numbers.

We might ask *now* for solutions to similar equations in which multiplication rather than addition is the operation. For instance, if three children are given five pieces of candy, there is likely to be an argument, since dividing the number of pieces of candy equally is impossible. This problem is similar to the question we considered in the last section. What we would like is a solution to the equation $3x = 5$. Unfortunately for the grownups present in the previous situation, there just is no integer x such that $3x = 5$. If there had been six pieces of candy, we would have had no difficulty, since there is an integer x, namely 2, such that $3x = 6$. In the last section we got around the difficulty by postulating the existence of solutions to equations which might not have them. In the present case we may do likewise.

This time, instead of ordered pairs of natural numbers, we *temporarily* represent the new numbers which are to be solutions by ordered pairs of integers. These new numbers are to have the property that they are solutions to equations of the form $bx = a$, where a and b are integers, $b \neq 0$.

We might proceed in exactly the same way to use the symbol (a, b), in which a and b are any integers, $b \neq 0$, for a number which satisfies the equation $bx = a$. Equality this time would have to be defined in such a way that $cbx = ca$ had the same solution as $bx = a$, $bc \neq 0$. (We would not want $2x = 4$ and $4x = 8$ to have different solutions.) Accordingly, we define $(a, b) = (c, d)$ if and only if $ad = bc$. If you glance back at the definition of equality for integers in the last section, you will notice that the only change is that multiplication replaces addition in the definition. Here we assume that addition and multiplication for integers are already known. For example, $3x = 5$ has the solution $(5, 3)$. This time the ordered pair $(5, 3)$ is one of the infinite class of equal ordered pairs which we will symbolize by $\frac{5}{3}$. Again, to pin down all the details is tedious and complicated. $(6, 3)$ is one of the members of the class we denote by $\frac{6}{3}$, which in turn may be identified with the natural number 2. In the end we obtain the set of *rational numbers*. These numbers furnish solutions to all equations $bx = a$, a and b integers, $b \neq 0$. Of course, these numbers have all the properties of the ordinary quotients of two integers, a/b, $b \neq 0$. Incidentally, it is easy to see why we do not divide by zero, since $a/0$ would be a solution to the equation $0 \cdot x = a$. If $a \neq 0$, there is clearly no solution, and even if $a = 0$, any rational number would be a solution. Since that would lead to all sorts of difficulties, we agree not to divide by zero. All the cleverness of all the mathematicians does not suffice to surmount this difficulty. Any definition which we might make costs more than it is worth in other desirable properties. Hence we settle for relinquishing the power to divide by zero.

Just as in the case of the integers, once we have made the point that rational numbers can be represented as ordered pairs of integers, we drop the subject and count on your long experience with fractions to help you with the manipulative rules for fractions which are all unchanged by this new formulation and its subsequent development. When all is said and done, we eventually end up with a system of numbers which is consistent with the following definition of the rational numbers.

Definition 3–4.1. The set of rational numbers is the set

$Q = \{x \mid x = m/n,\ m \text{ and } n \text{ are integers},\ n \neq 0\}$. ($Q$ stands for quotients of integers.)

For a geometric representation of the rationals, we return to the number line on which we have already set up a correspondence between certain points and the integers. To locate a point corresponding to m/n, where m and n are natural numbers, we take the distance from the point corresponding to 0 to the point corresponding to the natural number m and divide this line segment into n equal segments. We make the point at the end of the first such segment correspond to m/n. For example, $\frac{3}{2}$ is located by dividing the line segment from 0 to 3 into 2 equal segments; the end point of the first segment is identified with the rational number $\frac{3}{2}$.

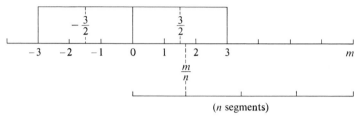

FIGURE 3–2

(Integers m may be written $m/1$, and their location is unchanged on the number line.) For rationals which are quotients of one positive and one negative integer, we recall that $-m/n = m/-n = -(m/n)$ (m and n natural numbers) and proceed as before. Divide the segment joining 0 and $-m$ into n equal segments; the end point of the first segment corresponds to $-m/n$. For example,

$$\frac{-3}{2} = \frac{3}{-2} = -\frac{3}{2}$$

is located to the left of 0, and $\frac{1}{2}$ the distance from 0 to -3. If both m and n are negative integers, $m/n = -m/-n$, and we obtain the same point as in the first case.

As before, "less than" for rational numbers means "to the left of" on the number line. For example,

$$\frac{3}{2} < 2, \quad \frac{-3}{2} < -1, \quad -2 < 1.$$

The rationals were devised to solve equations of the form $bx = a$, where a and b are integers, $b \neq 0$. As a bonus, with appropriate extensions of the definition of addition and multiplication, all equations of the form $bx = a$, where a and b are rational numbers, $b \neq 0$, also have solutions in the set of rational numbers. In fact, the set of rational numbers is *closed* under the operations of addition, multiplication, subtraction, and division (with the exception that we never divide by 0).

EXERCISES

[+]1. The *sum* of two rational numbers a/b and c/d is defined to be

$$\frac{a}{b} + \frac{c}{d} = \frac{ad + bc}{bd}.$$

Show that the sum of two rational numbers is again a rational number.
Find the sum of

(a) $\frac{3}{5}$ and $\frac{5}{7}$, (b) $\frac{3}{17}$ and $\frac{17}{19}$, (c) $\frac{-2}{3}$ and $\frac{17}{13}$.

[+]2. The *product* of two rational numbers a/b and c/d is defined to be

$$\frac{a}{b} \cdot \frac{c}{d} = \frac{ac}{bd}.$$

Show that the product of two rational numbers is a rational number. Find
the product of

(a) $\frac{2}{3}$ and $\frac{3}{4}$, (b) $\frac{-2}{5}$ and $\frac{15}{3}$, (c) 4 and $\frac{5}{4}$.

[+]3. The *difference* of two rational numbers a/b and c/d is defined to be

$$\frac{a}{b} + \left(-\frac{c}{d}\right).$$

Show that the difference of two rationals is again a rational number. Find
the difference of:

(a) $\frac{2}{3}$ and $-\frac{2}{3}$, (b) $\frac{2}{3}$ and $\frac{2}{3}$, (c) $\frac{3}{5}$ and $-\frac{7}{3}$.

[+]4. The *quotient* of two rational numbers a/b and c/d, $bcd \neq 0$, is defined
to be

$$\frac{a/b}{c/d} = \frac{a}{b} \cdot \frac{d}{c} = \frac{ad}{bc}.$$

Show that the quotient of two rational numbers is a rational number. Find
the quotient of

(a) $\frac{2}{3}$ and $\frac{3}{2}$, (b) $\frac{3}{2}$ and $\frac{-2}{3}$, (c) $\frac{17}{12}$ and $\frac{2}{3}$.

[+]5. Show that $a/b = ac/bc$, $bc \neq 0$, follows from the definition: $(a, b) = (c, d)$ if and only if $ad = bc$. Using this definition, show that

(a) $\frac{2}{4} = \frac{6}{12}$, (b) $\frac{3}{2} = \frac{-6}{-4}$, (c) $\frac{17}{30} = \frac{51}{90}$.

[+]6. If $p = kp_1$ and $q = kq_1$, where k is the *greatest common divisor* of p
and q, show that $p/q = p_1/q_1$, p_1 and q_1 having no common divisor except
1 and -1.

7. For positive rationals, i.e., rationals to the right of zero on the number line, $a/b < c/d$ if and only if $ad < bc$. Show that $\frac{2}{3} < \frac{3}{4}$.

8. Give a counterexample to show that the definition in Exercise 7 does not hold for rationals in general (i.e., rationals which are not necessarily positive).

*9. Show that between any two positive rationals, there is always another rational. [*Hint:* Suppose that $a < b$, and show that $a < (a+b)/2 < b$.]

3–5 THE REAL NUMBERS

In the last two sections we extended the number system, beginning with the *natural numbers*, $N = \{1, 2, 3, \ldots, n, \ldots\}$, to include solutions to equations of the form $b + x = a$, where a and b were any natural numbers. This extended set was called the *integers*,

$$I = \{\ldots, -3, -2, -1, 0, 1, 2, 3, \ldots\}.$$

Finally, to include solutions to equations of the form $bx = a$, a and b integers, $b \neq 0$, we made the extension from the integers to the *rationals*,

$$Q = \left\{ \frac{m}{n} \mid m \text{ and } n \text{ are integers, } n \neq 0 \right\}.$$

This greatly enlarged set suffices for most practical applications of numbers. We may measure the length of any line segment as accurately as we please, using only rational numbers. However, the ancient Greeks found that even this greatly extended set of numbers was not sufficient to meet all their requirements. It is true that these requirements were of a theoretical rather than a practical nature. The problem which they encountered was as follows: What is the length of the diagonal of a square whose sides have length 1? This problem is equivalent to finding the length of the hypot-

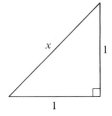

FIGURE 3–3

enuse of an isosceles right triangle with legs whose lengths are 1.

The Greeks had developed plane geometry to a considerable degree and had proved, using rigorous standards of logic, that the sum of the squares of the legs of a right triangle equals the square of the hypotenuse (the Theorem of Pythagoras). That is, $x^2 = 1^2 + 1^2$ or $x^2 = 2$. The difficulty is that one can show that there is no rational number x with the property that $x \cdot x = 2$.

Theorem 3–5.1

There is no rational number p/q such that $(p/q)^2 = 2$.

Proof: We proceed by contradiction. Suppose that there is a rational number $r = p/q$ such that $r^2 = 2$. We may suppose that any common factors of the integers p and q have been divided out. (See Exercises 5 and 6, Section 3–4.)

STATEMENT	REASON
1. $p^2/q^2 = 2$.	1. Hypothesis
2. $p^2 = 2q^2$.	2. If equals are multiplied by equals, the results are equal.
3. p^2 is even.	3. Definition of even (see Example 2–5.1)
4. p is even.	4. Example 2–5.2
5. $p = 2p'$.	5. Definition of even
6. $(2p')^2 = 4p'^2 = 2q^2$.	6. Substitution of equals for equals in step 2
7. $2p'^2 = q^2$.	7. Equals divided by equals, the results are equal.
8. q^2 is even.	8. Definition of even
9. q is even.	9. Example 2–5.2
10. Contradiction: both p and q are even, and therefore divisible by 2, but they have no common factors.	10. Hypothesis, steps 4 and 9

Since the assumption that there is a rational number p/q such that $(p/q)^2 = 2$ leads to a contradiction, there is no rational number whose square is 2.

It was clear to the Greeks that there certainly is a line segment whose length has the property that its square is 2, but their logic convinced them that it was not a rational number. This puzzle persisted for many centuries. The Greeks called such lengths "incommensurables."

After our experience of the last two sections, it is absolutely clear what a modern mathematician would do in such circumstances. He would simply extend his system of numbers to include solutions to the problem. The technique for this final extension is in one sense more sophisticated than either of the previous ones and we shall, as before, give only an indication as to one method of making this extension.

We assume that the number line with points corresponding to all rational numbers is available to us. The idea is to add numbers to our system which will measure lengths of any line segment which we can conceivably encounter, and, in particular, a number whose square is 2.

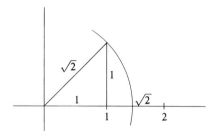

FIGURE 3–4

The technique bears only the faintest resemblance to our previous procedure used in obtaining the integers and the rationals.

For this discussion let the universal set be the set of rational numbers, Q. We now consider all possible partitions or separations of the set of rational numbers into pairs of disjoint sets A and $\overline{A}$, with the following properties:

1. $A \neq \emptyset; A \neq Q$.
2. Every element of A is less than every element of $\overline{A}$.
   (If $a \in A \land \overline{a} \in \overline{A}$, then $a < \overline{a}$.)
3. If $a \in A$, then there is an $a^* \in A$ such that $a < a^*$.

Each such set A determines a separation of the rationals into two sets; we shall call this separation a *Dedekind cut* and denote it by the symbol $(A \mid \overline{A})$. For example, if we let $A = \{r \mid r < 2\}, \overline{A} = \{r \mid r \geq 2\}$, and the cut in the number line occurs at the rational number 2.

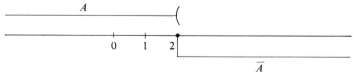

FIGURE 3–5

Accordingly, we identify each cut at a rational point with the corresponding rational number. However, to return to our original problem, suppose that we wanted a solution to the problem of finding a number whose square is exactly 2. We then define the set

$$A = \{r \mid r^2 < 2 \lor r \leq 0\}.$$

Then

$$\overline{A} = \{r \mid r^2 > 2 \land r > 0\},$$

since there is no rational whose square is exactly 2. This cut in the number line will occur at a distance from 0 which measures the hypotenuse of the right triangle with legs 1.

To complete the task, we would need to define equality for cuts. This is easily done: $(A \mid \overline{A}) = (B \mid \overline{B})$ if and only if $A = B$.

From this point on, the procedure would parallel the extensions we have previously made. We would next extend the definitions of addition and multiplication and their inverses, subtraction and division, to cuts so as to be consistent with the definitions which we have previously given for rational numbers. We have identified cuts which correspond to all the rational numbers. All the other cuts correspond to essentially new numbers which are called *irrational numbers*. The set of all cuts is called the *set of real numbers*. All the gaps in the rational number line are now filled in, and we have numbers which measure the lengths of every conceivable line segment. Some of these are numbers which solve problems similar to the problem of finding a solution to the equation $x^2 = 2$; others are of an essentially different kind. For example, the number which measures the length of the circumference of a circle with diameter 1 is not rational nor is it a solution of an equation like $x^2 = 2$. It is an example of a real number which is said to be *transcendental*. Again, to follow through on all the details would be tedious and complicated. Our interest here is not in the details, but simply in motivating the extension and in briefly suggesting the ideas involved in the extension.

There are still other extensions of the number system which have proved useful. *However from now on in this book, we shall understand that unless specifically stated otherwise, the word number means real number.*

EXERCISES

1. Give three examples of real numbers which are not rational.

2. Draw a Venn diagram showing the inclusion relations between the sets N (natural numbers), I (integers), Q (rational numbers), and R (real numbers).

3. Define the set A which would cut the rationals at $\sqrt{3}$.

*4. Show that $\sqrt{3}$ is not a rational number.

*5. Is 0.3333 . . . a rational number? a real number?

*6. Is there a real number x such that $x^2 + 1 = 0$? Explain.

3–6 SUMMARY

In this chapter we have attempted to indicate how it is possible to begin with a small number of undefined terms and a set of axioms which list the properties which we assume about these terms and proceed, making use of the machinery of sets and logic, to show that the undefined objects behave just as we would expect that *natural numbers* should.

Then as we considered the problem of finding solutions to equations of the form $b + x = a$, a and b natural numbers, we found the set of natural numbers to be insufficient. We then proceeded to postulate the existence of new numbers given in terms of the old which furnished solutions to this problem. These new numbers we called *integers*.

When this set proved insufficient to solve problems of the type $bx = a$, a and b integers and $b \neq 0$, we extended the notion of number to include solutions to such problems. This new set we called the set of *rational numbers*.

Finally, when this set proved inadequate to measure lengths of line segments which we knew existed, we made the extension to the set of *real numbers*.

In all these extensions, the focus has been on the idea that new definitions depending on previously developed concepts could be formulated which would furnish solutions to new problems.

In each case we hope that the idea was pushed only far enough to indicate how the extension could be made. It was not our intent to seriously pursue the new definition in sufficient detail for the reader to be able to calculate solutions to complicated problems dealing with each system. In fact, details were omitted on purpose so that it would be clear that our interest was not in the technical details, but simply in the ideas behind each extension.

We shall have occasion to use real numbers in much that follows, and we shall look at the connection between real numbers and decimal fractions in a later chapter.

REVIEW EXERCISES

1. Using the definition of addition for natural numbers,

(a) $n + 1 = n'$,   (b) $n + k' = (n + k)'$,

and the definitions

$$1' = 2, \quad 2' = 3, \quad 3' = 4, \quad 4' = 5,$$

show that

$$3 + 2 = 4 + 1.$$

2. Prove by mathematical induction that the sum of the first n even natural numbers is $n(n + 1)$.

3. Describe briefly but precisely the relation between Peano's postulates for the natural numbers and proofs by mathematical induction.

4. Give an ordered pair of natural numbers which represents the solution to each of the following equations.

(a) $2 + x = 3$.   (b) $4 + x = 3$.   (c) $3 + x = 3$.

5. What are the usual symbols for the integers which are the solutions to the equations in Exercise 4?

6. Give an ordered pair of integers which represents the solution to each of the following equations.

(a) $2x = 7$.   (b) $15x = -3$.   (c) $-2x = 5$.

7. Find three rational numbers between $\frac{1}{3}$ and $\frac{1}{2}$.

8. Prove that $1 + \sqrt{2}$ is an irrational number.

9. What set A of rational numbers defines the Dedekind cut identified with the real number $\sqrt{5}$?

10. Discuss the sense in which irrational numbers are impractical for measurement.

Suggested Readings

*DEDEKIND, R., "Irrational Numbers" in *The World of Mathematics*, edited by J. R. Newman, Simon and Schuster, New York, 1956, Vol. I, pp. 525–536.

*HEMPLE, C. G., "On the Nature of Mathematical Truth" in *The World of Mathematics*, edited by J. R. Newman, Simon and Schuster, New York, 1956, Vol. III, pp. 1619–1634.

KOEHLER, D., "The Ability of Birds to Count" in *The World of Mathematics*, edited by J. R. Newman, Simon and Schuster, New York, 1956, Vol. I, pp. 488–496.

*RICHARDSON, M., *Fundamentals of Mathematics*, Macmillan, New York, 1958, Ch. 14, pp. 418–428.

*TITCHMARSH, E. C., *Mathematics for the General Reader*, Doubleday Anchor Books, Garden City, N. Y., 1959, Chs. 4 and 6, pp. 48–58, pp. 75–83.

General References

ADLER, I., *The New Mathematics*, Signet, New York, 1960.

COURANT, R. and H. E. ROBBINS, *What Is Mathematics?*, Oxford University Press, New York, 1941, Chs. 1 and 2.

DUBISCH, R., *The Nature of Number*, Ronald Press, New York, 1952.

FUJII, J. N., *An Introduction to the Elements of Mathematics*, John Wiley, New York, 1961, Ch. 9, pp. 124–148.

HAFSTROM, J. E., *Basic Concepts in Modern Mathematics*, Addison-Wesley, Reading, Mass., 1961, Chs. 7, 8, and 9.

NCTM Twenty-third Yearbook, "The Concept of Number" by Ivan Niven, NCTM, Washington, 1957, pp. 7–35.

NEWMAN, J. R., *The World of Mathematics*, Simon and Schuster, New York, 1956, Vol. I, Part III.

NIVEN, I., *Numbers: Rational and Irrational*, Random House, New York, 1961.

THURSTON, H. A., *The Number System*, Interscience, New York, 1956.

4 | RELATIONS AND FUNCTIONS

4–1 RELATIONS

In the last chapter we used the concept of an *ordered pair* of objects. We remember that this was simply a pair, (a, b), in which it was important to distinguish the first member of the pair, a, from the second, b. For example, the ordered pair $(1, 2)$ is different from the ordered pair $(2, 1)$, even though they are made up of the same two elements.

The binary operations $\cap$ and $\cup$ were used in Chapter 1 to generate new sets from two given sets. For these operations, $A \cap B = B \cap A$ and $A \cup B = B \cup A$. The order in which the operations were performed turned out to be irrelevant. However, for many other operations, order is vitally important. Whether one first dons one's space suit and then goes outside the space ship or first goes outside the space ship and then puts on one's space suit might be unimportant on earth but very important on the moon.

A new operation on two sets which yields a third set is the *cartesian product* of the two sets.

Definition 4–1.1. Given two sets A and B, the *cartesian product of A and B, A $\times$ B*, is the set of all ordered pairs (a, b) in which $a \in A$ and $b \in B$.

EXAMPLE 4–1.1. Let $A = \{1, 2\}$ and $B = \{0, 1\}$.

$$A \times B = \{(1, 0), (1, 1), (2, 0), (2, 1)\}.$$

EXAMPLE 4–1.2. Let A be the set of even integers and B be the set of odd integers.

$$A \times B = \{(2n, 2m + 1) \mid n \text{ and } m \text{ are integers}\}.$$

Some elements of $A \times B$ are $(2, 1)$, $(0, 3)$, $(-4, 17)$, and $(-2, -3)$.

We have considered certain relations between sets: equality, equivalence, and inclusion. All these relations have the property that, given two sets, we are always able to tell whether one set is in the given relation to the other. In this sense, a relation can be thought of as a way of specifying another set, namely, the set of all ordered pairs of sets which are in this relation.

Instead of pursuing relations between sets, we wish to consider relations between elements in two sets, or more often in the same set. If we use "relation" in the ordinary way, the relation is known if, given two objects, we are able to decide whether or not the objects are in the relation. A relation, then, is usually given by a rule which determines a set of ordered pairs, namely, the ordered pairs of objects which are in this relation. For example, if we consider the ordered pair (Tom Jones, Mary Jones), it is clear that this pair is not in the relation "is the mother of," although (Mary Jones, Tom Jones) might very well be and (Mary Smith, Tom Jones) might conceivably be.

On the other hand, suppose that we have a set of ordered pairs $\{(a, b)\}$; we can always give a rule (a relation) which would determine this set. If no obvious rule does the trick, we could use the rule "a is related to b if and only if the ordered pair (a, b) appears in the given set." Therefore, if we have a rule giving a relation, we can arrive at a set of ordered pairs, or if we have a set of ordered pairs, we can formulate a rule giving the relation. Since the set of ordered pairs is always in the background anyhow, we find it more convenient for the purposes of this text to define the relation as the set, rather than the rule determining the set.

Definition 4–1.2. Given any two sets A and B, a relation ρ in $A \times B$ is a subset of $A \times B$.

EXAMPLE 4–1.3. Suppose that we are thinking of the relation of equality between real numbers. For the sets $A = \{1, 2\}$ and $B = \{0, 1\}$ of Example 4–1.1, the condition for (a, b) to be a member of this relation is that $a = b$. Hence the relation $\rho = \{(1, 1)\}$.

EXAMPLE 4–1.4. If the condition for membership were $<$, the subset of $A \times B$ which is determined would be $\emptyset$, since no element of A is less than any element of B.

EXAMPLE 4–1.5. For the same sets A and B, if the relation is $\rho = \{(1, 0), (2, 0), (1, 1), (2, 1)\}$, the rule determining this relation might have been "greater than or equal to."

Several rules may give the same subset of $A \times B$. Suppose that $A = B = \{1, 2\}$. The rule determining the relation ρ might be "$<$"; then $\rho = \{(1, 2)\}$. On the other hand, the relation ρ might have been $\rho = \{(x, y) \mid y = x + 1\}$; then $\rho = \{(1, 2)\}$.

This example also illustrates a situation which frequently arises; namely, the two sets A and B may be equal. *A relation in $A \times A$ is said to be a relation* on A.

Definition 4–1.3. Given a relation $\rho = \{(a, b)\}$ in $A \times B$, the set of a's or first elements is called the *domain* of the relation. The set of b's or second elements is called the *range* of the relation.

Suppose that the relation $\rho = \{(1, 2), (2, 3), (3, 4)\}$. The domain of the relation ρ is the set $D = \{1, 2, 3\}$. The range of the relation ρ is the set $R = \{2, 3, 4\}$. We may notice that all three sets ρ, D, and R are equivalent, but no two of them are equal. ρ and D and ρ and R are disjoint, while D and R overlap; in fact, $D \cap R = \{2, 3\}$.

In symbols the *domain* of the relation $\rho = \{(a, b)\}$ in $A \times B$ is

$$D = \{x \mid (x, b) \in \rho \text{ for some } b \in B\}.$$

The range is

$$R = \{y \mid (a, y) \in \rho \text{ for some } a \in A\}.$$

It is sometimes convenient to write $a \, \rho \, b$ instead of $(a, b) \in \rho$; for example, $a < b$, $a = b$.

EXERCISES

1. Given: $A = \{a\}$, $B = \{a, b\}$, $C = \{a, b, c\}$, $D = \{0\}$, $E = \{2, 4, 6\}$, $F = \{2, 4\}$. Find

(a) $A \times B$,	(b) $B \times A$,	(c) $B \times F$,
(d) $C \times D$,	(e) $E \times F$,	(f) $F \times E$.

2. Given that U is the set of natural numbers less than 5, which of the following is a relation in $U \times U$?

(a) $\{(1, 3), (2, 6), (3, 9)\}$.
(b) $\{(0, 3), (3, 2), (1, 4), (4, 1)\}$.
(c) $\{(3, 4), (4, 1), (3, 2)\}$.
(d) $\{(5, 1), (3, 2), (0, 3)\}$.
(e) $\{(1, 2), (1, 3), (1, 4), (2, 3), (2, 4), (3, 4)\}$.

3. Write three relations in $A \times B$ if $A = \{1, 2, 3\}$ and $B = \{5, 6, 7\}$.

4. What is the domain of each of the relations you defined in Exercise 3? What is the range?

5. Does "is the brother of" determine a relation in $U \times U$ if U is the set of all people? If U is the set of all males?

6. Does "is the daughter of" determine a relation in $U \times U$ if U is the set of all people?

7. Is every cartesian product $A \times B$, where $A \subset U$ and $B \subset U$, a relation in $U \times U$? Justify your answer.

8. Is every relation in $U \times U$ a cartesian product $A \times B$ for some $A \subset U$ and $B \subset U$? Justify your answer.

9. Let $U = \{1, 2, 3\}$ and let $\rho = \{(1, 2), (1, 1), (1, 3), (2, 1)\}$ be a relation on U. Is ρ a cartesian product $A \times B$ for some $A \subset U$ and some $B \subset U$?

10. If $\rho = \{(a, b)\}$ is a relation in $A \times B$, is the domain of ρ the set A? Is the range B? Explain.

⁺11. A relation having the following three properties is called an *equivalence relation*.

(a) $(a, a) \in \rho$ for all a in the domain of ρ.   (Reflexive)
(b) $[(a, b) \in \rho] \rightarrow [(b, a) \in \rho]$.   (Symmetric)
(c) $[(a, b) \in \rho \wedge (b, c) \in \rho] \rightarrow [(a, c) \in \rho]$.   (Transitive)

Which of the following are equivalence relations? If not, why not?

(i) $\{(1, 2), (2, 1), (1, 3)\}$.
(ii) $\{(1, 2), (2, 1), (1, 3), (3, 1)\}$.
(iii) $\{(1, 2), (2, 1), (1, 3), (3, 1), (1, 1), (2, 2), (3, 3)\}$.
(iv) The relation defined by "is the brother of."
(v) The relation defined by "lives in the same state as."

*12. For the set $S = \{A, B, C, D, E, \text{ and } F\}$, where the elements of S are the sets of Exercise 1, what is the relation ρ on S if

(a) the condition for membership in ρ is equality?
(b) the condition for membership in ρ is equivalence?
(c) the condition for membership in ρ is $\subset$?

*13. Define the cartesian product of three sets A, B, and C. Of n sets A_1, $A_2, \ldots, A_n$.

*14. Using the definitions in Exercise 13, list all the members of $U \times U \times U$ if $U = \{0, 1\}$. Of $A_1 \times A_2 \times \cdots \times A_n$ if $A_1 = A_2 = \cdots = A_n = \{1\}$.

4–2 VARIABLES, CONSTANTS, AND OPEN SENTENCES

Many people have the impression that mathematics is mysterious, obscure, and difficult. One of the reasons seems to be that mathematicians are always using symbols such as x, y, and z, which are frequently called *unknowns*, and others such as a, b, and c, which are also not known but are not called unknowns. By this time we are resigned to the fact that in mathematics we frequently do not know what we are talking about, and we even like to think that at times this is an advantage. However, we did agree that the undefined terms would be listed in advance. The others should be intelligible, since we make precise statements about the way in which they are to be used.

A symbol which in a given context stands for exactly one specific thing is called a *constant*. The symbol 2 is a constant. Moreover, the symbols a, b, c, $\ldots$ (that is, letters at the beginning of the alphabet) have traditionally been used as symbols for numbers which are fixed in a given discussion but not specifically named; they are always understood to be constants.

On the other hand, we have frequently used the symbol x (for example, $N = \{x \mid x$ is a natural number$\}$) to stand for *any* element of a given set. Such a symbol is called a *variable*. The set is called the range of the variable, and any member of the set is called a *value* of the variable. Traditional symbols for variables are the letters toward the end of the alphabet, such as x, y, and z. (It is perhaps unfortunate that "range" is traditionally used in two ways; we have called the set of all second elements of the ordered pairs belonging to a relation the *range* of the *relation*. Now we also call the set of values over which a variable "ranges" the *range* of the *variable*. If, however, we remember that the term is used in these two ways, we may avoid some natural confusion. We usually state quite explicitly "*range* of the *relation*" or "*range* of the *variable*" when using the term.)

In Chapter 2 a *statement* was defined as a sentence which was either true or false, but not both. We gave the rather contrived example, "This sentence is false," as a sentence which is not a statement. There are many other sentences, however, which are not statements: "He is a hangman," "$x \in S$," "x is the first man to orbit the earth." None of these sentences is a statement because we cannot tell whether the sentence is true or false until we know what "he" and "x" stand for. If "he" stands for Reinhard Heydrich, we might say that the first sentence is true, but if "he" stands for Albert Schweitzer, we would certainly say it is false. We shall call sentences in which variables like "he" or "x" appear *open sentences*; they are neither true nor false. Only when a meaningful value of the variable is substituted for the variable does the sentence become a statement. The set of values of the variable (or variables) for which an open sentence is true is called the *solution set* for the open sentence.

Much of mathematics is concerned with the problem of finding solution sets for open sentences.

> EXAMPLE 4-2.1. $x^2 = 4$. x is a variable in the open sentence $x^2 = 4$; 4 is a constant. Suppose that we agree that the universal set is the set of real numbers. The range of x is then the set of all real numbers, since any real number is a meaningful value of the variable x. For when we substitute any real number for x in the sentence $x^2 = 4$, we get a statement; for example $3^2 = 4$ and $(-2)^2 = 4$ are statements. The first is false, the second is true. The solution set for the open sentence $x^2 = 4$ is $\{2, -2\}$.

An open sentence may contain more than one variable; for instance, $xy = 2$. If U is the set of all natural numbers, then the solution set of this sentence is

$$\{(x, y) \mid xy = 2\} = \{(1, 2), (2, 1)\}.$$

If U is the set of all real numbers, the solution set would be

$$\left\{ \left(2r, \frac{1}{r} \right) \mid r \text{ is a nonzero real number} \right\}.$$

Suppose that we are given an open sentence containing two variables, say x and y. Let the range of x be a subset of A and the range of y be a subset of B, then the open sentence has for a solution set a subset of $A \times B$. However, since any subset of $A \times B$ is a relation in $A \times B$, the solution set of the open sentence is a relation. In the same way, every open sentence containing two variables defines a relation, namely, the solution set of the open sentence.

EXERCISES

1. Which of the following are statements and which are open sentences. Identify the variables in the open sentences.

      (a) $3 + 4 = 5$.
      (b) $x + 4 = 5$.
      (c) He is a student.
      (d) Richard Nixon is president of the United States.
      (e) The Indian Ocean is salty.
      (f) She and I are going to a ball tonight.

2. For each of the following open sentences, give the range of each variable and the solution set of the open sentence.

      (a) $2x + 3 = 5$.
      (b) $2x = x + x$.
      (c) $x + y = y + x$.
      (d) If x takes Math I, x works hard. (U is the set of all college students.)
      (e) $x = 4 \lor x < 3$. (Take U to be the set of natural numbers.)
      (f) $p \lor \sim p$.
      (g) $p \rightarrow p$.
      (h) If A is the set of all natural numbers < 4, $(x, 1) \in A \times A$.

3. If U is assumed to be the set of all real numbers, find the solution sets of the following open sentences.

      (a) $x^2 = 2 \land x > 0$.
      (b) $x - 1 = 0 \land x < 1$.
      (c) x is prime and x is even.
      (d) $x \, R \, 2 \land x$ is a natural number $\land R$ is "less than."
      (e) $\{(x, 1)\} \subset \{1\} \times U$.

4. What is the relation defined by each of the following open sentences?

      (a) x is the brother of y.
      (b) x is the mother of y.
      (c) $x + y = 2$.
      (d) $x^2 + y^2 = 1 \land xy = 0$.
      (e) $(x < y) \land (x$ and y are integers $< 3)$.

4–3 FUNCTIONS

We now come to a second basic idea in mathematics. The first was the idea of a set. We developed the concept of number from that of set and have used numbers, relations between sets, and operations on sets in discussing proof by induction, number systems, and solution sets for open sentences. All of the preceding developments have been closely connected with sets. The second basic concept is that of function.

While a social function is sometimes a pleasant occasion, and a smoothly functioning piece of machinery may be admired, the disciplinary function of the dean of students is not usually contemplated with great joy. In the preceding sentence, the uses of the word function suggest (1) a collection of people, (2) a right relation between the parts of a machine, and (3) an interaction between persons. If we use a word in mathematics, we naturally abstract the best of all its meanings, always trying to state as precisely as possible just how the word shall be used.

As was the case with conditional statements, mathematicians have used the function idea for many years and have developed several different ways of saying the same thing. The idea involved is very similar to the idea of a relation. In fact, sometimes we see the expression functional relation; the layman might be pardoned for thinking that this means an especially useful or efficient sort of relation. The mathematician's use of the word function is just that—a rather special kind of relation.

Definition 4–3.1. Given two nonempty sets A and B, a *function* is a subset, F, of $A \times B$ with the property that no two distinct ordered pairs belonging to F have the same first element.

EXAMPLE 4–3.1. Let

$$A = \{1, 2, 3, 4, 5\} \quad \text{and} \quad B = \{2, 3, 4, 5, 6\}.$$

Then $F = \{(1, 4), (2, 5), (3, 6)\}$ is a function, while

$$\rho = \{(1, 4), (1, 6), (2, 4), (3, 4)\}$$

is a relation but not a function.

As a consequence of our definition, every function is a relation, but not every relation is a function.

Since a function is a special kind of relation, we use the expressions *domain* and *range of a function* in the same way in which the terms were used for a relation, namely, to refer to the set of first elements and the set of second elements, respectively, of the ordered pairs belonging to the function. Note that the sets A and B in Definition 4–3.1 above are usually not the domain and range of the function. However, the domain is always a subset of A and the range a subset of B.

In Example 4–3.1 above, the domain of F is $D_F = \{1, 2, 3\}$, which is a subset of A, and the range of F is $R_F = \{4, 5, 6\}$, which is a subset of B. Similarly, the domain of ρ is $D_\rho = \{1, 2, 3\}$, and the range of ρ is $R_\rho = \{4, 6\}$.

Just as in the case of a relation, this formulation of the concept of function is a relatively recent one, and the older phrases used to convey the same idea all refer to the rule for forming the set of ordered pairs rather than to the set itself.

Thus in other sources you will find a function referred to as a "rule," a "correspondence" between two sets, a "mapping" of one set into another set. Or, in older texts, you will find "given a value of the variable x, if a corresponding value of a second variable y can be found, we say that y is a function of x." If we examine each of these closely, we find that we are always led to consider a set of ordered pairs; and, conversely, given a set of ordered pairs, we can "formulate a rule," "set up a correspondence between 2 sets," or "map one set into another set," etc.

There is one other feature of our definition which should be mentioned. In many texts no distinction is made between a relation and a function. In some of these cases, relations which are not functions by our definition are called multiple-valued functions, and functions (in our sense) are called single-valued functions. Each of these other formulations has a historical *raison d'être*, and a brief look at other formulations may be helpful.

We have already discussed the rule aspect of a function in Section 4–1 (Relations); that is, the set of ordered pairs is determined by a rule, and a rule may be devised which determines a given set of ordered pairs.

The "correspondence" idea is essentially the same as matching elements of one set (the domain) with those of another (the range), as we did in discussing equivalent sets, except that we do not insist on a one-to-one correspondence. Several elements of the first set may be matched with a single element of the second set. We have also met the idea of correspondence in our attempt to picture the real numbers. There we established a correspondence between the real numbers and the points on a line.

The word mapping has a special connotation and indicates a geo-metric way of thinking of a function. Diagrams can sometimes be drawn showing how one set is mapped into another.

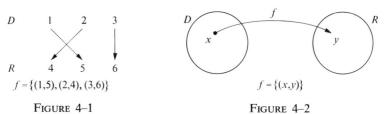

$$f = \{(1,5), (2,4), (3,6)\}$$

FIGURE 4-1

$$f = \{(x,y)\}$$

FIGURE 4-2

You will notice, in this way of describing a function, that the arrows go from points in set D to points in set R; for this reason we sometimes see the terminology, f *maps D onto R*.

Still another picture is that of a "black box" or "machine" which takes *in* an element $x \in D$ and puts *out* an element $y \in R$.

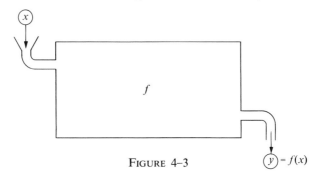

FIGURE 4-3

$$y = f(x)$$

In all these ways of formulating the idea behind a function, we are led to a set of ordered pairs $\{(x, y)\}$ where x comes from a given set D and y belongs to some set R. The property which distinguishes a func-tion from a relation is that if f is a function, then

$$[(x, y) \in f \wedge (x, z) \in f] \rightarrow y = z.$$

There are several suggestive notations in use for functions. We shall depart only slightly from tradition. We shall use letters f, g, h, and occasionally F, G, H, etc., to stand for a function; for example,

$$f = \{(x, y) \mid y = x^2\} \qquad \text{or} \qquad g = \{(n, p_n) \mid p_n \text{ is the } n\text{th prime}\}.$$

It is both useful and traditional to denote the second member of an ordered pair belonging to a function f, whose first member is x, by

$f(x)$. This notation, introduced by Euler in 1734, is extremely efficient and convenient.

If $f = \{(x, y)\}$, we let $y = f(x)$, and write $f = \{(x, f(x))\}$. The variable x used to denote the first member of the ordered pair is usually called the *independent variable*. The second member of the ordered pair, y, is usually called the *dependent variable*, and writing $y = f(x)$ enables us to indicate clearly the value of y corresponding to a particular value of x.

For instance, suppose that $f = \{(x, y) \mid y = x^2\}$; then $f(2) = 4$ indicates in an especially convenient way that $(2, 4) \in f$.

Strictly speaking, of course, $f = \{(x, y) \mid y = x^2\}$ does not define the function f unless the domain of f (that is, the range of the variable x) is specified. However, *henceforth let us agree that unless otherwise specified, the domain of a function is the largest possible subset of the set of real numbers*.

As was the case for a relation, a function is frequently defined by an open sentence in two variables. In many cases, the open sentence will take the form $y = f(x)$; for example, $y = x + 2$ or $f(x) = x^2 - 1$. Of course, for a function to be defined, in addition to an open sentence, we need to know the domain of the function (i.e., the range of the independent variable). However, the domain is usually clear from the context, or it is a subset of the set of real numbers, as indicated in our agreement above. In other cases it should be given explicitly.

For the function f defined by $y = f(x) = x + 2$, it follows from our agreement that the domain of f is $D = \{x \mid x \text{ is a real number}\}$, and the range is the set $R = \{y \mid y = \text{a real number}\}$. In this case, $D = R = $ the set of all real numbers. On the other hand, for the function f defined by $f(x) = x^2 - 1$, the domain D is the set of real numbers, and the range R is the set of real numbers greater than or equal to -1.

EXERCISES

1. Which of the following relations are functions?
   - (a) $\{(1, 1), (0, 1), (2, 1)\}$.
   - (b) $\{(1, 1), (1, 0), (1, 2)\}$.
   - (c) $\{(x, y) \mid y = x\}$.
   - (d) $\{(x, y) \mid y = x^2\}$.
   - (e) $\{(x, y) \mid y^2 = x\}$.
   - (f) $\{(x, y) \mid y = 16 - x^2\}$.
   - (g) $\{(x, y) \mid x^2 + y^2 = 1\}$.

2. List three elements belonging to the function $f = \{(x, y)\}$ defined by each of the following open sentences.

(a) y is the mother of x.
(b) $y = x^2 + 2x + 1$.
(c) $y = \sqrt{x}$.
(d) $y = (x - 1)/x$.
(e) $y = 2^x$.
(f) y is the xth letter of the Greek alphabet.
(g) $y + x = 8$.   (h) $y = 3/(x^2 - 4)$.

Determine the domain and the range of the functions in parts (a), (b), (f), (g), and (h) above.

3. Translate the following symbols into words. Which of these are incorrect uses of the notation, and why?

(a) $(1, 2) \subset F$.   (b) $(2, 3) \in A \times B$.   (c) $2 \rho 3 \leftrightarrow (3, 2) \in \rho$.
(d) $f(x) \in f$.   (e) $x F F(x)$.

4. From the context determine a reasonable domain, and write the function in set notation for the functions defined by:

(a) f maps the even integer $2n$ onto the integer n,
(b) g is the correspondence $x \rightarrow x + 1$,
(c) $f(n) = 1/n$,
(d) y is the year in which x became the world's heavyweight champion.
(e) $f(n) = (-1)^n$.

What is the range of each function?

5. Which of the following open sentences defines a function?

(a) $y < x$.
(b) $x + y = 1$.
(c) $\sqrt{x} = y$.
(d) $X \subset Y$. (U is the set of all sets.)
(e) y is the age of x.
(f) y is the sex of x.
(g) y is the child of x.
(h) y is the father of x.

6. If $f = \{(x, 2x + 1)\}$, find:

(a) $f(0)$,   (b) $f(-1)$,   (c) $f(100)$,
(d) $f(-x)$,   (e) $f(a)$,   (f) $f(x + h)$.

7. If $f(x) = x^2 - 1$ and $g(x) = 2 - 3x$, find:

(a) $f(1)$,   (b) $g(3)$,   (c) $f(1) + g(2)$,
(d) $f(4) + g(1)$.   (e) $f(g(1))$ (f) $g(f(a))$,
(g) $f(x + h) - f(x)$,   (h) $g(x + h) - g(x)$.

8. If $f = \{(x, x)\}$ and $g = \{(x, x^2/x)\}$, are f and g the same function? Explain.

9. If $T(x)$ is the truth value of x, what are the domain and range of T?

*10. Do the set operations of union, intersection, and complementation define functions? Specify the domain and range of each.

11. Is $\{(x, y) \mid y = 1$ if x is rational $\wedge \; y = 0$ if x is irrational$\}$ a function?

4-4 GRAPHS OF FUNCTIONS AND RELATIONS

It is often helpful to have a picture of a relation or function in $A \times B$. If the sets A and B are the real numbers, then a method devised by the French philosopher and mathematician René Descartes (1596–1650) has proved to be enormously helpful and productive. This scheme is the basis for that part of mathematics known as analytic geometry. It is sometimes called cartesian geometry, in honor of Descartes.

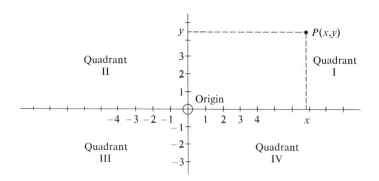

The simple but ingenious device consists of taking two real number lines intersecting at right angles and setting up a one-to-one correspondence between ordered pairs of real numbers and points in the plane in the following way. Given any ordered pair of real numbers, say (x, y), locate x on the horizontal number line, the x-axis, and y on the vertical number line, the y-axis. The point P, in which the line through x perpendicular to the x-axis meets the line through y perpendicular to the y-axis, is associated with the ordered pair (x, y). Conversely, given any point P in the plane, construct lines through P parallel to the x-axis and the y-axis. The ordered pair associated with P is then (x, y), where x is the point in which the line through P parallel to the y-axis meets the x-axis, and y is the point in which the line through P parallel to the x-axis meets the y-axis.

The numbers x and y are called, respectively, the *abscissa* and *ordinate* of the point P. The two together are called the *coordinates* of the point P. The point of intersection of the two axes is called the *origin of coordinates*, or just the *origin*, and the four divisions into which the plane is divided are called *quadrants*.

Thus we have associated with every point in the plane exactly one ordered pair of real numbers and with every ordered pair of real numbers exactly one point in the plane. This one-to-one correspondence allows us to picture geometrically sets of ordered pairs of real numbers or to describe analytically (by means of sets of ordered pairs of real numbers) sets of points in the plane.

Definition 4-4.1. The *graph* of a *function* or *relation* is the set of points whose coordinates make up an ordered pair belonging to the function or relation.

We now consider a few special functions and relations and their graphs.

EXAMPLE 4-4.1

$I = \{(x, y) \mid y = x\} = \{(x, x)\}$.

This is sometimes called the *identity function*, since it pairs every real number with itself. The set of all real numbers is both the domain and the range of the function I.

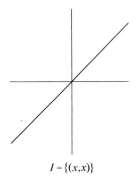

$I = \{(x,x)\}$

EXAMPLE 4-4.2

$f = \{(x, y) \mid y = x^2\} = \{(x, x^2)\}$.

The domain is the set of all real numbers. The range is the set of all non-negative real numbers.

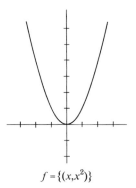

$f = \{(x,x^2)\}$

EXAMPLE 4–4.3

$$\rho = \{(x, y) \mid y < x\}.$$

The domain of ρ is the set of all real numbers. The range of ρ is the set of all real numbers.

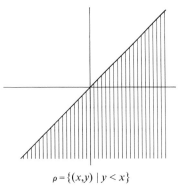

$\rho = \{(x,y) \mid y < x\}$

EXAMPLE 4–4.4

$$f = \{(x, f(x)) \mid f(x) = x \text{ if } x \geq 0, \quad f(x) = -x \text{ if } x < 0\}.$$

This is called the *absolute value function* and $f(x)$ is written $|x|$. The domain is the set of all real numbers; the range is the set of all nonnegative real numbers.

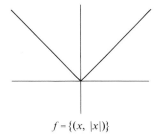

$f = \{(x, |x|)\}$

EXAMPLE 4–4.5

$$f = \{(x, y) \mid y \text{ is the greatest integer} \leq x\}.$$

This function is called the *greatest integer function*, and $f(x)$ is written $[x]$. The domain is the set of all real numbers; the range is the set of all integers.

We have seen above that the range of a function or relation need not be the set of all real numbers; neither is the domain of a function or relation always the set of all real numbers.

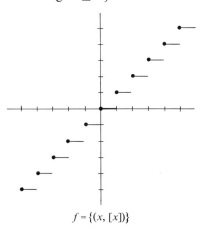

$f = \{(x, [x])\}$

EXAMPLE 4-4.6

$$\rho = \{(x, y) \mid x^2 + y^2 = 1\}.$$

The domain of ρ = range of ρ = $\{x \mid |x| \leq 1\}$.

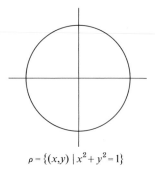

$\rho = \{(x,y) \mid x^2 + y^2 = 1\}$

EXAMPLE 4-4.7

$$\rho = \{(x, y) \mid y^2 = x\}.$$

The domain of $\rho = \{x \mid x \geq 0\}$. The range of ρ is the set of all real numbers.

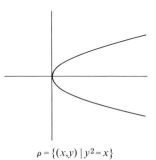

$\rho = \{(x,y) \mid y^2 = x\}$

EXAMPLE 4-4.8

$$f = \{(x, y) \mid y = \sqrt{x}\}.$$

The domain of $f = \{x \mid x \geq 0\}$. The range of $f = \{x \mid x \geq 0\}$. (The symbol $\sqrt{x}$ is defined to mean a real number y such that $y^2 = x$ and $y \geq 0$.)

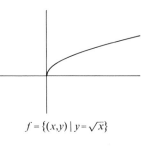

$f = \{(x,y) \mid y = \sqrt{x}\}$

EXERCISES

1. Sketch the graph of each of the following relations and functions.
    (a) $\{(0, 1), (1, 0), (1, 1), (0, 0)\}$.
    (b) $\{(x, 2x)\}$.
    (c) $\{(x, x + 1)\}$.
    (d) $\{(x, y) \mid y = |x| + 1\}$.
    (e) $\{(x, y) \mid y = 4 - x \wedge x$ and y are natural numbers$\}$.
    (f) $\{(x, y) \mid y = x \wedge 0 < y < 1\}$.

2. Which of the following graphs are graphs of functions?

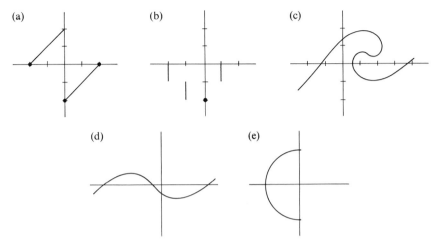

(a)　　　　(b)　　　　(c)

(d)　　　　(e)

*3. Sketch the graph of:

(a) f defined by $f(x) = 1$ if x is irrational, and $f(x) = 0$ if x is rational;

(b) $f = \{(x, y) \mid y < x \text{ if } x \geq 0 \wedge y > x \text{ if } x < 0\}$;

(c) $f = \{(x, y) \mid |x| + |y| = 0\}$;

(d) $f = \{(x, y) \mid |x| + |y| = 1\}$;

(e) $f = \{(x, y) \mid y = [x] + x\}$.

4. If $f(x) = x + 1$, sketch the graph of each of the following:

(a) $\{(x, f(x))\}$.　　　(b) $\{(-x, f(x))\}$.　　　(c) $\{(x, f(-x))\}$.

(d) $\{(x, -f(x))\}$.　　　(e) $\{(x, f(x) - 1)\}$.　　　(f) $\{(x - 1, f(x))\}$.

$^+$5. The graph of a function or relation is said to be *symmetric with respect to the y-axis* if $(x, f(x)) \in f \to (-x, f(x)) \in f$. Which of the following are symmetric with respect to the y-axis?

(a) $f = \{(x, y) \mid y = x\}$.　　　　　　(b) $f = \{(x, y) \mid y = x^2\}$.

(c) $f = \{(x, y) \mid y = |x|\}$.

(d) $f = \{(x, y) \mid y = \sqrt{1 + x^2}\}$.

(e) $f = \{(x, y) \mid y^2 = x\}$.

$^+$6. Can the graph of a function be symmetric with respect to the x-axis? (See Exercise 5.) Explain.

7. Show that $|a| \cdot |b| = |ab|$.

8. If $x \geq 0$, $\sqrt{x}$ is defined to be a nonnegative number y such that $y^2 = x$. Sketch the graph:

(a) $\{(x, y) \mid y = \sqrt{4 - x}\}$.　　　(b) $\{(x, y) \mid y = -\sqrt{1 + x^2}\}$.

What is the domain of each function?

4–5 CONVERSE OF A RELATION AND INVERSE FUNCTIONS

It is possible to form new functions or relations from given ones in much the same way that we did with sets and statements.

Definition 4–5.1. The *converse of a relation* $\rho = \{(x, y)\}$ is the set of pairs $\rho^* = \{(y, x)\}$.

It follows from this definition that the converse of a relation is a relation. The *range* of the *relation* becomes the *domain* of the *converse* relation, while the *domain* of the *relation* becomes the *range* of its *converse*.

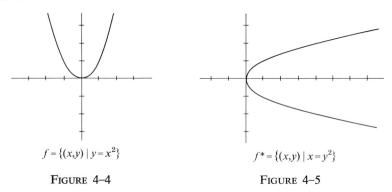

$f = \{(x,y) \mid y = x^2\}$ $f^* = \{(x,y) \mid x = y^2\}$

FIGURE 4–4   FIGURE 4–5

If we consider a function as a relation, it is a fair question to ask, "Is the converse of a function a function?" The following example shows that the answer is, not necessarily.

Let the function $f = \{(x, y) \mid y = x^2\}$. The domain of f is the set of all real numbers. The range of $f = \{y \mid y \geq 0\}$. (See Fig. 4–4.)

The converse of f is $\{(y, x) \mid y = x^2\}$ or $\{(x, y) \mid x = y^2\}$, which is a relation but not a function. The domain of the converse is $\{x \mid x \geq 0\}$. The range of the converse is $\{y \mid y$ is a real number$\}$. (See Fig. 4–5.)

Definition 4–5.2. If the converse of a function f is a function, it is called the *inverse* of the function f and is denoted by f^{-1}.

One nice consequence of our definitions is that the graph of the converse is especially easy to obtain. Since the converse of $f = \{(x, y)\}$ is simply $\{(y, x)\}$, if we take any point (x, y) on the graph of f, then (y, x) is on the graph of the converse.

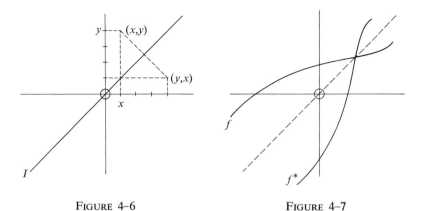

FIGURE 4–6   FIGURE 4–7

However, from Fig. 4–6 it is clear that (y, x) is the reflection of (x, y) in the graph of the identity function $I = \{(x, x)\}$. Since every point on the converse of f is the reflection of a point of f in this line, to draw the graph of the converse, we simply reflect the graph of f in the line which is the graph of the identity function. (See Fig. 4–7.)

Inverse functions play an important role in many parts of mathematics. A look at the graph of a function suffices to tell us whether or not the function has an inverse. If for any value of the dependent variable y there is more than one ordered pair (x, y) belonging to the function f, then the converse of the function is a relation but not a function, and consequently the function has no inverse. Geometrically, this means that if any horizontal line intersects the graph of f at more than one point, the function has no inverse.

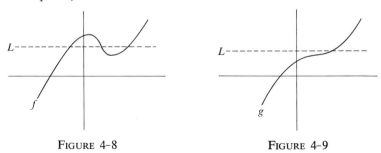

FIGURE 4–8   FIGURE 4–9

The function f in Fig. 4–8 does not have an inverse function, since there are horizontal lines (for example, line L) which intersect f more than once. The function g in Fig. 4–9 does have an inverse because no horizontal line intersects the graph of g more than once.

EXERCISES

1. What is the converse of each of the following relations ρ?
   (a) $\{(x, y) \mid y = -x + 1\}$.
   (b) $\{(0, 1), (1, 0)\}$.
   (c) $\{(x, y) \mid y = x^2 \land x < 0\}$.
   (d) $\{(x, x + 1)\}$.
   (e) y is the husband of x.
   (f) y is a parent of x.
   (g) y is a sibling of x.

2. Find the domain and range of each of the relations in Exercise 1.

3. Which of the relations of Exercise 1 are functions? Which of the converse relations are functions? Which of the converse relations are inverse functions?

4. What is the converse of the relation:
   (a) $<$?   (b) $\{(x, -x)\}$?   (c) ρ^* ?   (d) $\leq$?   (e) $\{(x, |x|)\}$?

5. Which of the following functions has an inverse? Sketch the graph of the function and its inverse, if it has one.

   (a) $\{(x, x)\}$.   (b) $\{(x, 2x + 1)\}$.   (c) $\{(x, |x|)\}$.
   (d) $\{(x, [x])\}$.   (e) $\{(x, x^2)\}$.   (f) $\{(x, \sqrt{x})\}$.

4–6 LINEAR FUNCTIONS AND THEIR GRAPHS

Functions may be classified in many ways. Perhaps the simplest kind of function is the function $f = \{(x, c)\}$. Such a function is called a *constant function*, since for any value of the independent variable x, the value of the function is always the same number c.

EXAMPLE 4–6.1. $f = \{(x, 2)\}$. f can be defined by the equation $f(x) = 2$.

In the last section we considered one way of generating a new function or relation from a given one; namely, the converse of a relation and, in certain cases, the inverse of a function. If we are given two functions, new functions may be found in several different ways. We may form the sum, the difference, the product, or the quotient of two functions.

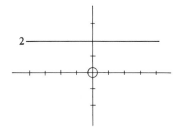

Definition 4–6.1. Given two functions f and g,

$$f + g = \{(x, f(x) + g(x))\};$$
$$f - g = \{(x, f(x) - g(x))\};$$
$$f \cdot g = \{(x, f(x) \cdot g(x))\};$$
$$\frac{f}{g} = \left\{\left(x, \frac{f(x)}{g(x)}\right)\right\}.$$

The domain of $f + g$, $f - g$, $f \cdot g$, and f/g is the intersection of the domains of f and g, except that in the case of f/g, we must exclude from the domain those values of x for which $g(x) = 0$.

EXAMPLE 4–6.2. Let $f = I = \{(x, x)\}$, the identity function of Example 4–4.1, and $g = \{(x, 2)\}$, the constant function of Example 4–6.1.

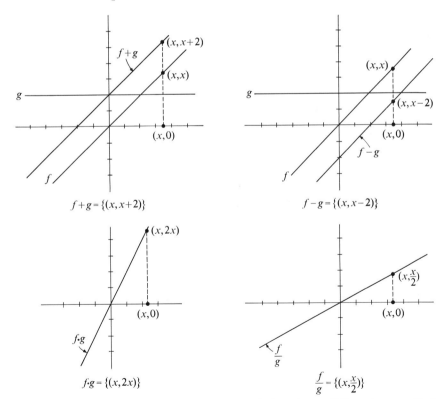

Each of the preceding is a member of the class of functions called *linear functions*.

Definition 4-6.2. A function

$$f = \{(x, mx + b) \mid m \text{ and } b \text{ are real numbers } \wedge m \neq 0\}$$

is called a *linear function*.

Linear is an appropriate name for such functions, since the graph of a linear function is a straight line.

In Euclidean plane geometry, line is one of the basic undefined terms. However, everyone feels intuitively that he knows what is meant by "straight line." In Euclidean geometry straightness is one of the characteristic properties of lines, and this notion is intimately related to the idea of the direction of one point in the plane from another. One way of specifying the direction of one point from another is given in the following definition.

Definition 4-6.3. Given two points, $P_1(x_1, y_1)$ and $P_2(x_2, y_2)$, the *slope of the line segment* $\overline{P_1P_2}$ is $(y_2 - y_1)/(x_2 - x_1)$.

This measure of direction is the quotient of the difference of the ordinates and the difference of the abscissas of the two points. We say that it determines the direction of P_2 from P_1, since if we start at P_1 and go $(x_2 - x_1)$ horizontal units and $(y_2 - y_1)$ vertical units, we arrive at P_2.

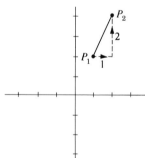

EXAMPLE 4-6.3. Find the slope of the line segment joining the points $(1, 2)$ and $(2, 4)$.

$$\frac{y_2 - y_1}{x_2 - x_1} = \frac{4 - 2}{2 - 1} = 2.$$

Starting at $P_1(1, 2)$, $x_2 - x_1 = 1$, and we go 1 unit to the right and $4 - 2 = 2$ units up to arrive at $P_2(2, 4)$.

EXAMPLE 4-6.4. Find the slope of
the line segment $\overline{P_1P_2}$ if P_1 is $(1, 2)$
and P_2 is $(-1, -2)$.

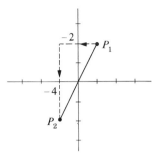

$$\frac{y_2 - y_1}{x_2 - x_1} = \frac{-2 - 2}{-1 - 1} = \frac{-4}{-2} = 2.$$

Starting at P_1, we go 2 units to the
left and 4 units down to arrive at P_2.

You will note in these two examples that although the slope in both
cases is 2, in Example 4-6.3 we went 1 unit to the right and 2 units up
to arrive at P_2, while in Example 4-6.4 we went to the left 2 units and
down 4 units to get to P_2. In both cases the slope of the line segment
$\overline{P_1P_2}$ is the same. However, the difference in the way of getting from
P_1 to P_2 was caused by the relative positions of P_1 and P_2, P_2 being
to the right of P_1 in the first example and to the left in the second.
These examples show that the slope is independent of the order in which
we take P_1 and P_2.

$$\frac{y_2 - y_1}{x_2 - x_1} = \frac{-(y_1 - y_2)}{-(x_1 - x_2)} = \frac{y_1 - y_2}{x_1 - x_2}.$$

To support our statement that the graph of a linear function

$$f = \{(x, mx + b)\}$$

is a straight line, we are able to show that the line segment joining any
two points on the graph of a linear function $\{(x, mx + b)\}$ always has
the same slope, namely m.

Let P_1 be $(x_1, mx_1 + b)$ and P be any other point $(x, mx + b)$ on
the graph of f. Then the slope of $\overline{P_1P}$ is

$$\frac{mx + b - (mx_1 + b)}{x - x_1} = \frac{m(x - x_1)}{x - x_1} = m,$$

and every point of the graph of f different from P_1 lies on a line segment
$\overline{P_1P}$ with slope m.

EXAMPLE 4-6.5. Sketch the graph of the linear function
$\{(x, 2x + 1)\}$. The points $(0, 1)$ and $(1, 3)$ lie on the graph
of f.

Although we have defined only the slope of a line segment, since the graph of a linear function $f = \{(x, mx + b)\}$ is a straight line and since every line segment $\overline{P_1P_2}$ joining two points on f has slope m, we say that the *slope of the line is m.*

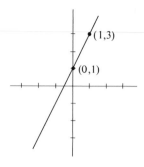

EXERCISES

1. For each of the following pairs of functions f and g, form $f + g$, $f - g, f \cdot g, f/g$.

    (a) $f = \{(x, 0)\}, g = \{(x, 2)\}$.
    (b) $f = \{(x, x)\}, g = \{(x, b)\}$.
    (c) $f = \{(x, 2x + 2)\}, g = \{(x, -2x + 2)\}$.
    (d) $f = \{(x, x^2)\}, g = \{(x, x - 2)\}$.
    *(e) $f = \{(x, \sqrt{x})\}, g = \{(x, \sqrt{-x})\}$.

2. What are the domains of each of the functions $f, g, f + g, f - g, f \cdot g$, and f/g in Exercise 1 above?

3. Find the slope and sketch the graph of each of the linear functions:

    (a) $f = \{(x, 2x + 3)\}$;   (b) $f = \{(x, -x - 1)\}$;
    (c) $f = \{(x, x/2 + 1)\}$;   (d) $f = \{(x, -x/3 + 1)\}$.

4. Is $f = \{(x, |x|)\}$ a linear function? Explain.

5. Find the linear function and sketch its graph if:

    (a) the slope of f is 2 and $(1, 2) \in f$;
    (b) $(0, 2) \in f$ and $(1, 1) \in f$;
    (c) $(1, 1) \in f$ and $(-1, 0) \in f$;
    (d) $m = 2$ and $(0, 2) \in f$;
    (e) $(0, 0) \in f$ and $(3, 1) \in f$.

6. Is the set $\{(1, y) \mid y \text{ is a real number}\}$ a function? a relation? Sketch its graph.

+7. Find the linear function whose graph passes through the points with coordinates $(a, 0)$ and $(0, b)$.

+8. Find the linear function whose graph passes through the points with coordinates (x_1, y_1) and (x_2, y_2).

9. Find the function whose graph is parallel to the graph of the function $f = \{(x, 2x + 3)\}$ and passes through the origin.

10. If the slopes of two lines are $\frac{1}{2}$ and 2, which line is "steeper"?

11. Is $f = \{(x, 3)\}$ a linear function? Sketch its graph. What can you say about the slope of the line segment joining any two points on the graph of f?

*12. The points $A(0, 0)$, $B(4, 6)$, and $C(13, 0)$ are vertices of a right triangle. Find the slope of line segments $\overline{AB}$ and $\overline{BC}$. Do you notice anything?

*4–7 POLYNOMIALS

Any linear function $F = \{(x, mx + b)\}$ can be thought of as a function obtained from two constant functions and the identity function by multiplication and addition. If we let $f = \{(x, m)\}, g = \{(x, x)\}$, and $h = \{(x, b)\}$, then

$$F = \{(x, mx + b)\} = f \cdot g + h.$$

In much the same way other important functions can be generated.

EXAMPLE 4–7.1. If $I = \{(x, x)\}$, then

$$F = I \cdot I = I^2 = \{(x, x^2)\}.$$

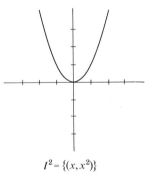

$I^2 = \{(x, x^2)\}$

EXAMPLE 4–7.2. If $I = \{(x, x)\}$, then

$$F = \{(x, a)\} \cdot I^2 + \{(x, b)\} \cdot I + \{(x, c)\}$$
$$= \{(x, ax^2 + bx + c)\}.$$

F is defined by the equation $F(x) = ax^2 + bx + c$.

The function F of Example 4–7.2 is called the general quadratic function. Its graph is a *parabola*.

If we continue building new functions by multiplication and addition from the identity function and constant functions, we arrive at a function which takes the following form.

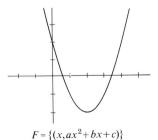

$F = \{(x, ax^2 + bx + c)\}$

Definition 4–7.1. A *polynomial function* or *polynomial of degree n* is a function

$$p = \{(x, a_nx^n + a_{n-1}x^{n-1} + \cdots + a_1x + a_0) \mid a_n \neq 0\}.$$

A defining equation for the function is

$$p(x) = a_nx^n + a_{n-1}x^{n-1} + \cdots + a_1x + a_0.$$

The sum and difference and product of two polynomial functions are again a polynomial function. A function formed by taking the quotient of two polynomial functions is called a *rational function*. A rational function is defined by the equation $r(x) = p(x)/q(x)$, where p and q are polynomials.

The domain of a polynomial function is the set of all real numbers; the domain of a rational function is the set of all real numbers x for which $q(x)$ is not zero.

The importance of polynomials in mathematics cannot be over-estimated. Polynomials are often used to approximate other functions. These approximations are particularly useful, since polynomials are relatively simple, well-behaved functions. In succeeding chapters, we shall look more closely at the graphs of these functions.

EXERCISES

1. Given the function $I = \{(x, x)\}$, $f = \{(x, 2)\}$, and $g = \{(x, -1)\}$, write in set form the polynomials:

   (a) $I^2f + gI + f$;   (b) $I^3 + 2fgI^2 - 2I - g$;   (c) $I^2 + 2I - f$.

What is the degree of each polynomial?

2. If $p(x) = 1 - x + x^2 - x^3$, what is $p(0)$? $p(1)$? $p(-x)$? $p(x + h)$?

3. Show that the sum of two polynomials is a polynomial. What is the degree of the sum polynomial?

4. Show that the product of two polynomials is a polynomial. What is the degree of the product polynomial?

5. Is a linear function a polynomial?

+6. If $p(x)$ defines a polynomial and $p(z) = 0$, then z is called a *zero* of the polynomial or a *root* of the polynomial equation $p(x) = 0$. Find the zeros of:

   (a) $p(x) = x + 1$;   (b) $p(x) = x^2 + 1$;   (c) $p(x) = x^2 - 1$;

(d) $p(x) = x^2 + x - 2$;   (e) $p(x) = x^3 - x$;
(f) $p(x) = x^4 + 1$.

+7. If $p(x) = ax^2 + bx + c$, then the point $(-b/2a, p(-b/2a))$ is called the *vertex* of the *parabola*, which is the graph of the function p. Find the vertex of the parabola given by:

(a) $p(x) = x^2 + x + 1$;   (b) $p(x) = 3x^2 - x + 2$;
(c) $p(x) = x^2 - 1$;   (d) $p(x) = 2x^2 - x - 1$;
(e) $p(x) = x^2 + 1$.

*8. Show that if $p(x) = ax^2 + bx + c$, then $p(-b/2a + h) = p(-b/2a - h)$.

9. Show that $p(x) = ax^2 + b$ is symmetric with respect to the y-axis. (See Section 4–4, Exercise 5.)

10. Sketch the graph of the functions defined in Exercise 7, using the results in Exercises 7, 8, and 9.

REVIEW EXERCISES

1. Find the solution set to the open sentence $|x - 1| = 1$.

2. What is the cartesian product of $A = \{0, 1\}$ and $B = \{2, 3, 4\}$?

3. Is the relation $\{(0, 1), (1, 2), (3, 1), (2, 3)\}$ a function? What is the domain of the relation? the range?

4. What is the converse of the relation in Exercise 3 above? Is the converse a function? What is its domain? its range?

5. Sketch the graph of the function f if
(a) $f(x) = [x]/2$;   (b) $f(x) = 2x - |x|$.

6. If f is defined by the equation $f(x) = 2 - x + 3x^2$, find $f(1), f(-1), f(\frac{1}{6})$. What is the domain of the function? What is its range?

7. Sketch the graph of the function defined by $x = 2y$. What is its inverse? Draw the graph of the inverse function.

8. If the function f is defined by the open sentence $f(x) = x^2 + 1$ and g is defined by $g(x) = -2x + 1$, find:
(a) $f(-1)$,   (b) $g(-1)$,   (c) $f(g(-1))$,   (d) $g(f(-1))$,
(e) $f(-1) \cdot g(-1)$,   (f) $f(a + b)$,   (g) $g(x + h) - g(x)$.

9. Find the linear function whose graph passes through the points $(1, 2)$ and $(3, 7)$.

10. Sketch the graph of the inverse of the function whose graph is shown on the right.

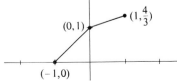

Suggested Readings

ALLENDOERFER and OAKLEY, *Principles of Mathematics*, Second Edition, McGraw-Hill, New York, 1963, Ch. 6, pp. 187–218.

*EVENSON, A. B., *Modern Mathematics*, Scott, Foresman and Co., Chicago, 1962, Chs. 5 and 6, pp. 75–140.

FUJII, J. N., *An Introduction to the Elements of Mathematics*, John Wiley, New York, 1961, Chs. 12 and 13, pp. 181–219.

*LUCE, R. D., "Some Basic Mathematical Concepts" in *Studies in Mathematics*, Vol. I, School Mathematics Study Group, Yale University, New Haven, Conn., 1959, Ch. 2, pp. 47–55, pp. 74–80.

*THIELMAN, H. P., "On the Definition of Functions," *The American Mathematical Monthly*, Vol. 60 (1953), p. 259.

General References

MAY, K. O., *Elements of Mathematics*, Addison-Wesley, Reading, Mass., 1959, Ch. 5.

STOLL, R. R., *Sets, Logic and Axiomatic Theories*, Freeman, San Francisco, 1961, Ch. 1.

TITCHMARSH, E. C., *Mathematics for the General Reader*, Doubleday Anchor Books, Garden City, N. Y., 1959, Ch. 12, pp. 140–151.

5 | SEQUENCES AND LIMITS

5–1 SEQUENCES

Definition 5–1.1. A *sequence* is a function whose domain is the set of natural numbers.

It is implicit in the definition that the set of ordered pairs which is the sequence contains infinitely many elements; for, corresponding to every natural number n, there is an ordered pair belonging to the sequence. For this reason such a function is frequently referred to as an *infinite sequence*.

> EXAMPLE 5–1.1. Let s be defined by $s(n) = 1$. The sequence is $\{(n, 1)\}$. A part of the graph of s is given in Fig. 5–1.

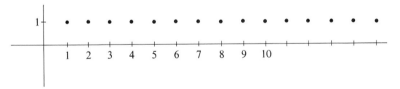

FIGURE 5–1

A sequence is usually defined by an expression giving the value of the function for any value n of the independent variable. The values of the dependent variable $y = s_n$† are called the *terms* of the sequence,

---

† The notation s_n for the value of the function s corresponding to the value n of the independent variable, rather than the usual functional notation $s(n)$, which we used in Chapter 4, is traditional and helps to distinguish sequences from other functions. We read the symbol s_n as s sub-n, and the letter n is called a subscript.

and s_n is called the *general term* of the sequence. It is a special property of the functions called sequences that there is a natural one-to-one correspondence between the set of natural numbers and the terms of the sequence. This natural correspondence establishes a natural order for the terms of the sequence; consequently, we speak of the first term of the sequence, the second term, the nth term, etc.

EXAMPLE 5-1.2. Let the sequence s be defined by

$$s(n) = s_n = 1/n;$$

that is, $s = \{(n, y) \mid y = s_n = 1/n\}$.

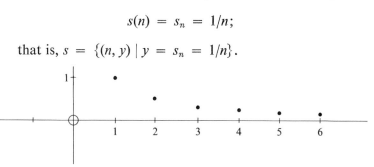

A sequence may also be defined by a *recursion formula*. (The definitions for addition and multiplication of natural numbers in Section 3–1 were given by recursion.)

EXAMPLE 5-1.3. $s = \{(n, s_n) \mid s_1 = 1 \wedge s_{n+1} = s_n + 2\}$. The first few terms of this sequence are 1, 3, 5, 7, 9. The nth term may be represented by $s_n = 2n - 1$.

The preceding example is a special case of a more general kind of sequence called an *arithmetic sequence*. In general, if the terms of a sequence are obtained recursively by adding a constant to the preceding term, the terms of the sequence are said to be in *arithmetic progression*. If we denote the first term of the arithmetic progression by A_1 and the constant by d, then

$$A_2 = A_1 + d, \qquad A_3 = A_2 + d = (A_1 + d) + d = A_1 + 2d.$$

It is easy to prove by mathematical induction that $A_n = A_1 + (n - 1)d$. (See Exercise 1 of the exercises for this section.)

EXAMPLE 5-1.4. Suppose that a beginning teacher in a certain school system receives a starting salary of $5000 a year and an increase of $300 a year. What will be his salary after 10 years?

Solution. Let $A_1 = \$5000$ and $d = \$300$. The problem is equivalent to finding A_{11}, the teacher's salary in his eleventh year with the system. By the formula $A_n = A_1 + (n - 1)d$ for $n = 11$, we have $A_{11} = \$5000 + 10(\$300) = \$8000$. The teacher's salary after 10 years will be $8000.

Another important kind of sequence is one in which any term after the first is obtained by multiplying the preceding term by a constant. Such sequences are called *geometric sequences,* and the terms of the sequence are said to be in *geometric progression.*

EXAMPLE 5-1.5. Let

$$s = \{(n, s_n) \mid s_1 = 1 \wedge s_{n+1} = 1.04 s_n\}.$$

The first few terms of this sequence are 1, 1.04, 1.04^2, 1.04^3, and 1.04^4. Again, it is easy to show by mathematical induction that $s_n = 1.04^{n-1}$. (a^0 is defined to be 1 if $a \neq 0$.)

In general, if we denote the first term of a geometric sequence by G_1 and the constant multiplier by r, the terms of the sequence are G_1, rG_1, r^2G_1, ... The term G_n may be shown to be $r^{n-1}G_1$ by mathematical induction. (See Exercise 2 below.)

In Example 5-1.5 above, the term s_n of the sequence may be interpreted as the amount which accumulates in $(n - 1)$ years if $1 is invested at 4% interest compounded annually.

As a final example of a sequence defined recursively, we mention the Fibonacci sequence, named for Leonardo Fibonacci, who lived in Italy around the beginning of the thirteenth century, and who was one of the few talented mathematicians of the Middle Ages.

EXAMPLE 5-1.6

$$U = \{(n, u_n) \mid u_1 = u_2 = 1, u_n = u_{n-1} + u_{n-2} \text{ for } n > 2\}.$$

The first few terms of the Fibonacci sequence are 1, 1, 2, 3, 5, 8, and 13.

This sequence has many interesting properties. In his book, *Liber abaci,* one of the important books on mathematics produced during the Middle Ages, Fibonacci gives the following problem.

How many pairs of rabbits can be produced from a single pair in a year if it is supposed that every month each pair begets a new pair which from the second month on becomes productive?

A few minutes' thought about this problem shows that its solution leads to the Fibonacci sequence. (See Exercise 6.)

Other surprising occurrences of Fibonacci's sequence are found in nature: the number of buds counted in a spiral fashion around a twig, or similar counts on pine cones or sunflowers. (See references at the end of the chapter for more detailed accounts.)

EXERCISES

1. Prove by mathematical induction that the general term A_n of the arithmetic sequence

$$A = \{(n, A_n) \mid A_{n+1} = A_n + d\}$$

is given by $A_n = A_1 + (n - 1)d$.

2. Prove by mathematical induction that the general term G_n of the geometric sequence

$$G = \{(n, G_n) \mid G_{n+1} = rG_n\}$$

is given by $G_n = r^{n-1}G_1$.

3. Find the first five terms of the sequence defined by:
   (a) $s_1 = 2 \land s_{n+1} = \frac{1}{2}s_n$;
   (b) $s_1 = 2 \land s_{n+1} = s_n + 2$;
   (c) $s_n = (-1)^n$;
   (d) $s_n = 1 + (-1)^n$;
   (e) $s_n = 1 + 1/n$;
   (f) $s_n = 1/(n^2 + 1)$.

4. Find a formula for the general term of the sequences in (a) and (b) of Exercise 3 above.

5. Find the first ten terms of Fibonacci's sequence.

6. Solve the problem of the rabbits from Fibonacci's *Liber abaci*.

7. Check that the formula

$$u_n = \frac{(1 + \sqrt{5})^n - (1 - \sqrt{5})^n}{2^n\sqrt{5}}$$

holds for the first two terms of the Fibonacci sequence. It can be shown that this formula gives the correct result for all natural numbers n.

*8. Show that $u_n \cdot u_{n+2} - u_{n+1}^2 = (-1)^{n+1}$ for the Fibonacci sequence.

9. Find the amount of $1000 invested at 4% compounded semiannually at the end of 5 years.

10. If one saved 1 cent the first week, 2 cents the second week, 4 cents the third week, and 2^{n-1} cents the nth week, how much would one have saved in 3 months?

5–2 THE LIMIT OF A SEQUENCE

In the last section, most of the sequences were defined either by giving an expression for the general term or by giving the general term by means of a recursion formula.

The sequences which are of most interest to us in succeeding sections are sets of ordered pairs coming from the cartesian product $N \times R$, where N is the set of natural numbers and R is the set of real numbers.

For many such sequences, it happens that for large values of n, s_n gets arbitrarily close to some number L.

For example, if we recall Example 5–1.2 in which $s_n = 1/n$, s_n is very small for large values of n. $s_{100} = 0.01$ and $s_{1,000,000} = 0.000001$. In fact, while s_n is never zero, we can make s_n as close to zero as we like by taking n large enough. For this reason the number zero is called the *limit of the terms of the sequence s*, or simply the *limit of the sequence*. In general, if the values of s_n for all sufficiently large values of n are as close as we please to a number L, we say that L is the limit of the sequence s and write $\lim s_n = L$.

EXAMPLE 5–2.1

$$s_n = 1 + \frac{(-1)^n}{n^2}.$$

n	1	2	3	4	5	6	7	8	9	10
s_n	0	$\frac{5}{4}$	$\frac{8}{9}$	$\frac{17}{16}$	$\frac{24}{25}$	$\frac{37}{36}$	$\frac{48}{49}$	$\frac{65}{64}$	$\frac{80}{81}$	$\frac{101}{100}$

For n large enough, s_n is as close to 1 as we please; hence $\lim s_n = 1$.

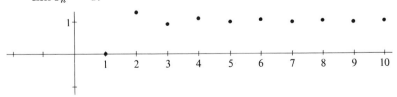

In the two examples given above, it is fairly clear that the limit of the sequence exists and that in the first case it is zero and in the second 1. In Example 5–1.1, in which $s_n = 1$, since the value of s_n is 1 for all n, lim $s_n = 1$.

On the other hand, in Example 5–1.3, $s_n = 2n - 1$, and it is clear that there is no number L such that s_n is close to L for all large values of n. On the contrary, we find values of s_n as large as we please if we take n to be large enough. However, sometimes the question is not so clear. Suppose that $s_n = n/(n^2 + 1)$. For large values of n, both n and $n^2 + 1$ get as large as we please, and it isn't clear that the quotient $n/(n^2 + 1)$ gets close to any number. For cases like this, and even much more complicated ones, we need a more precise definition of what we mean by a limit. To make explicit what "as close as we please" and "sufficiently large values of n" mean, we make the following definition.

Definition 5–2.1. If, given any arbitrarily small number $\epsilon > 0$, there exists a natural number N such that $|s_n - L| < \epsilon$ for all $n > N$, we say that the *limit of the sequence s is L*; and write
$$\lim s_n = \lim_{n \to \infty} s_n = L.$$

This rather formidable looking definition is the result of many years of effort on the part of mathematicians. The early practitioners had only the rather vague notion we began with; their good sense and instinctive feeling for the situation usually saved them from error, although they were without a clear understanding of just what it meant to say that the limit of s_n is L. However, in time strange and baffling statements came out of this rather hazy formulation, and mathematicians felt the need for a more explicit agreement about what a limit was.

Definition 5–2.1 is just a precise way to say that s_n is as close to L as we please if n is large enough. If we decide in advance how close we want to insist that s_n be to L (the measure of this closeness is the number ϵ), then we must say how large n must be in order to be sure that s_n is closer to L than ϵ. A geometric picture will help.

We plot the graph of the sequence s and the constant function $L = \{(x, L)\}$. If we insist that the values s_n of the function s be within ϵ of L, points on the graph must lie in a thin strip of width 2ϵ centered about the line L for all values of n to the right of N on the x-axis. The important aspect of the definition is that for *any* ϵ, no matter how

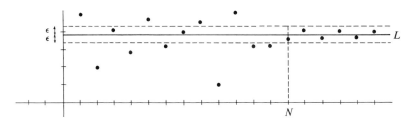

small, we must be able to give such an N. The traditional notation is $\lim_{n \to \infty} s_n = L$, read "the limit of s_n, as n approaches infinity, is L." The notation $n \to \infty$ is somewhat misleading because it seems to indicate that n approaches some largest integer; ∞ is not a natural number but merely a symbol used in this context to indicate that we are interested only in all very large values of n, that is, values of n greater than some preassigned natural number. Another way of reading $\lim_{n \to \infty} s_n = L$ is, "the limit of s_n, as n increases without bound, is L."

In the example, $s_n = n/(n^2 + 1)$, the limit L is actually 0. If we take $\epsilon = \frac{1}{2}$, then $N = 1$ will suffice; for if $n > 1$, then

$$s_n = \frac{n}{n^2 + 1} < \frac{1}{2} = \epsilon.$$

Similarly, if $\epsilon = \frac{1}{10}$, $N = 9$ will do, since for $n > 9$, then

$$s_n < \frac{10}{10^2 + 1} = \frac{1}{10.1} < \frac{1}{10} = \epsilon.$$

In fact, for any $\epsilon > 0$, if we take $N = [1/\epsilon]$, then for $n > N$, $s_n < \epsilon$. (If $N = 1/\epsilon$,

$$s_N = \frac{N}{N^2 + 1} = \frac{1/\epsilon}{1/\epsilon^2 + 1} = \frac{\epsilon}{1 + \epsilon^2} < \epsilon$$

and $s_n < s_N$ for $n > N$.)

If $\lim_{n \to \infty} s_n = L$, we say that the sequence s *converges* to the limit L. If the limit fails to exist, then we say that the sequence *diverges*.

EXAMPLE 5–2.2. $s_n = (-1)^n$. This sequence diverges, since $s_n = 1$ for even n, and $s_n = -1$ for odd n, and, consequently, no matter how large we take n, the terms of the sequence continue to hop back and forth between 1 and -1 and never stay close to any number L.

EXAMPLE 5–2.3. $s_n = n$. This sequence also diverges, since s_n is as large as we please if n is large. We sometimes see the notation $\lim\limits_{n\to\infty} s_n = \infty$. This is simply another way of saying that s_n gets arbitrarily large for large n and in no way signifies that there exists a real number L which is the limit of $s_n = n$.

EXERCISES

1. Write the first five terms of the sequence defined by:

(a) $s_n = 2^n$;   (b) $s_n = 1 - 1/n$;   (c) $s_n = \dfrac{1 + (-1)^n}{2}$;

(d) $s_n = 2/n^2$;   (e) $s_n = 1 + 2n$;   (f) $s_n = 2(\tfrac{1}{4})^n$;

(g) $s_n = 2^n/n$.

2. Decide whether the following sequences converge. If the sequence converges, find its limit, if you can.

(a) $\{(n, 1/n^2)\}$.   (b) $\{(n, 1 - 1/n^2)\}$.

(c) $\{(n, 1 + 2n)\}$.   (d) $\{(n, (\tfrac{1}{2})^n)\}$.

(e) $\left\{\left(n, \dfrac{1 - (-1)^n}{2}\right)\right\}$.   (f) $\left\{\left(n, 1 - \left(\dfrac{-1}{n}\right)^n\right)\right\}$.

3. If $s_n = 1 - 1/n$, find $L = \lim\limits_{n\to\infty} s_n$. If $\epsilon = \tfrac{1}{10}$, find N such that for $n > N$, $|s_n - L| < \tfrac{1}{10}$.

4. If $G_1 = 100$ and $G_{n+1} = \tfrac{1}{2}G_n$, what is $\lim G_n$?

*5. If $s_1 = 1$ and $s_{n+1} = s_n + 1/n$, what is $\lim s_n$?

*6. Show that $\lim\limits_{n\to\infty} c \cdot s_n = c \lim\limits_{n\to\infty} s_n$, provided that $\lim\limits_{n\to\infty} s_n$ exists.

*7. Show that $\lim\limits_{n\to\infty} (s_n + t_n) = \lim\limits_{n\to\infty} s_n + \lim\limits_{n\to\infty} t_n$, provided that $\lim\limits_{n\to\infty} s_n$ and $\lim\limits_{n\to\infty} t_n$ exists.

5–3 REAL NUMBERS AS LIMITS OF SEQUENCES OF RATIONALS

In Chapter 3, when we considered the extensions of the number system, we remarked that the rational numbers sufficed for approximating the length of any given line segment, but that there were segments whose lengths could not be measured exactly by any rational number, in particular the diagonal of a square with sides of length one.

The ordinary decimal representation of real numbers, if we content ourselves with finitely many decimal places, gives only rational approximations for most numbers. For example,

1.25 $= \frac{5}{4}$;

1.333 $= \frac{1333}{1000}$, which is an approximation for the rational number $\frac{4}{3}$;

1.414 $= \frac{707}{500}$, which is a rational approximation for $\sqrt{2}$;

3.14 $= \frac{157}{50}$, which is a rational approximation for π;

3.1416 $= \frac{3927}{1250}$, which is a slightly better rational approximation for π.

In fact, the decimal representation of any real number may be looked upon as representing the number as the limit of a convergent sequence of rationals.

When viewed in this light, the sequences are of three kinds.

1. There are decimals which terminate after a finite number of decimal places. For example, $0.25 = \frac{1}{4}$. Such decimals could be considered as sequences in which all terms after a finite number at the beginning were equal to each other. In the example 0.25, $s_1 = \frac{2}{10}$, $s_2 = \frac{25}{100}$, $s_n = \frac{25}{100}$ for $n \geq 2$. Characteristic of these terminating decimals is the fact that the digit 0 is assumed to stand in all decimal places after an initial finite number of places.

2. Some decimals eventually consist of a repeating finite pattern of digits. For example, 2.131313 .... . This number may be thought of as being the limit of the sequence

$$ s = \left\{ (n, s_n) \mid s_1 = 2 \wedge s_{n+1} = s_n + \frac{13}{100^n} \right\}. $$

The first few terms of this sequence are 2, 2.13, 2.1313, 2.131313, and 2.13131313.

3. Finally, there are decimals which never endlessly repeat any finite pattern of digits, for example, 1.01001000100001 .... . This number may be thought of as the limit of the sequence

$$ s = \left\{ (n, s_n) \mid s_1 = 1 \wedge s_{n+1} = s_n + \frac{1}{10^{n(n+3)/2}} \right\}. $$

Since decimals of the first kind may be thought of as repeating decimals, in which the pattern of digits repeated consists of the single digit 0, the first two kinds are not essentially different. These decimals represent rational numbers, while all irrational numbers are represented by decimals of the third kind.

For decimals of the first kind, the limit of the sequence is the rational number which is the general term of the sequence from some point on. In the example given above,

$$s_n = \tfrac{25}{100} \text{ for } n \geq 2 \lim s_n = \tfrac{25}{100} = \tfrac{1}{4}.$$

In order to see that the limit of a sequence of the second kind is a rational number, we need an expression for the general term which depends only on n and not on the preceding term. If

$$s_1 = 2, \ s_2 = 2 + \tfrac{13}{100}, \ s_s = 2 + \tfrac{13}{100} + \tfrac{13}{1000}, \text{ etc.},$$

we notice that to get the next term each time, we add a term of the geometric sequence

$$\frac{13}{100}, \ \frac{13}{10,000}, \ \frac{13}{1,000,000}, \ \cdots$$

In fact, it is not difficult to see that

$$s_n = 2 + \frac{13}{100} + \frac{13}{10,000} + \cdots + \frac{13}{100^{n-1}}.$$

If we knew the sum of the first $(n - 1)$ terms of the geometric progression, we would have an expression for s_n from which we could compute the limit. However, this was Exercise 4 in Section 3–2. If the geometric progression is $1, r, r^2, \ldots, r^{n-1}$, the sum of the first n terms is $(1 - r^n)/(1 - r)$ for $r \neq 1$. Accordingly,

$$s_n = 2 + \frac{13}{100} + \frac{13}{10,000} + \cdots + \frac{13}{100^{n-1}}$$

$$= 2 + \frac{13}{100}\left(1 + \frac{1}{100} + \frac{1}{10,000} + \cdots + \frac{1}{100^{n-2}}\right)$$

$$= 2 + \frac{13}{100}\left[\frac{1 - (1/100)^{n-1}}{1 - 1/100}\right]$$

$$= 2 + \frac{13}{100}\left(\frac{100 - 1/100^{n-2}}{99}\right)$$

$$= 2 + \frac{13}{99} - \frac{13}{99}\cdot\frac{1}{100^{n-1}},$$

and

$$\lim_{n\to\infty} s_n = 2 + \frac{13}{99} = \frac{211}{99},$$

since the term containing $1/100^{n-1}$ can be made as small as we please by taking n large enough.

In a similar fashion, every repeating decimal can be considered to be an infinite sequence of rationals which has a rational number as its limit.

Conversely, given any rational p/q, if we change the number into its decimal form, the digits eventually repeat. The reason for this phenomenon is that for any natural number q, there are only finitely many possible remainders $0, 1, 2, \ldots, q - 1$ when p is divided by q. Consequently, either the division comes out even, in which case the representation is a terminating decimal, or after at most $q - 1$ divisions, the remainder must be one previously obtained, and the pattern of digits in the quotient begins to repeat.

EXAMPLE 5–3.1. Obtain decimal representations for $\frac{1}{16}$ and for $\frac{1}{7}$.

$$
\begin{array}{r}
0.0625 \\
16\overline{)1.0000} \\
96 \\
\hline
40 \\
32 \\
\hline
80 \\
80 \\
\hline
\end{array}
\qquad
\begin{array}{r}
0.142857 \\
7\overline{)1.000000} \\
7 \\
\hline
30 \\
28 \\
\hline
20 \\
14 \\
\hline
60 \\
56 \\
\hline
40 \\
35 \\
\hline
50 \\
49 \\
\hline
1
\end{array}
$$

$$\tfrac{1}{16} = 0.0625$$

In the case of $\frac{1}{16}$, the decimal terminates and zeros repeat endlessly; in the case of $\frac{1}{7}$, we obtain all possible remainders 1, 2, 3, 4, 5, 6 (in the order 1, 3, 2, 6, 4, 5,) before getting a repetition of the remainder. After the remainder 1 reappears, the digits in the quotient and their corresponding remainders repeat. The traditional notation for indicating a repeating decimal is to put a bar over the pattern of repeating digits, for example, $\frac{1}{7} = 0.\overline{142857}$.

For nonrepeating decimals, it is a difficult task to specify the limit for the corresponding sequence of rational approximations. That a limit does exist is intuitively obvious from the following kind of geometric argument.

As an example, suppose that we consider the sequence of rational approximations for the number given above:

$$ S = \left\{ (n, s_n) \mid s_1 = 1 \wedge s_{n+1} = s_n + \frac{1}{10^{n(n+3)/2}} \right\}. $$

It is clear that (1) all terms of the sequence are ≥ 1; (2) for all n, $s_{n+1} > s_n$; (3) $s_n < 2$ for all n.

If we try to imagine the set A which would determine the cut in the rationals corresponding to this number, then

> A contains all rationals ≤ 1, while $\overline{A}$ contains all rationals ≥ 1.1;
>
> A contains all rationals ≤ 1.01, while $\overline{A}$ contains all rationals ≥ 1.02;
>
> A contains all rationals ≤ 1.01001, while $\overline{A}$ contains all rationals ≥ 1.01002; etc.

A rational belongs to A if and only if it is less than some s_n belonging to the sequence s defined above.

In general, if a sequence is bounded (i.e., if there is some number N such that $s_n < N$ for all n) and nondecreasing (that is, $s_{n+1} \geq s_n$ for all n), then it is a convergent sequence and has a limit. Every nonrepeating as well as every repeating decimal can be considered to be a sequence having these properties.

Consequently, another way of obtaining the real numbers from the set of rationals would have been to consider the set of all nondecreasing, bounded sequences of rationals. The set of limits of all such sequences would also have given us the set of real numbers.

EXERCISES

1. Give three rational approximations (quotients of integers) for
   (a) $\sqrt{2}$,   (b) $\sqrt{3}$,   (c) π.

2. Give three decimal approximations for

(a) $\frac{1}{32}$,   (b) $\sqrt{2}$,   (c) π,   (d) $\frac{1}{3}$,   (e) $\frac{1}{17}$,   (f) $\sqrt{2}/2$.

3. Find the repeating decimal which would define a sequence of rationals for which the limit is

(a) $\frac{2}{7}$,   (b) $\frac{1}{13}$,   (c) $\frac{2}{3}$,   (d) $\frac{1}{19}$.

4. Write the following rational numbers as repeating decimals:

(a) $\frac{4}{15}$,   (b) $\frac{4}{3}$,   (c) $\frac{2}{11}$,   (d) $\frac{1}{6}$,   (e) $\frac{17}{19}$.

5. Find the rational number whose decimal expansion is

(a) $0.\overline{14}$,   (b) $0.6\overline{78}$,   (c) $1.\overline{123}$,   (d) $2.\overline{1}$,   (e) $0.0\overline{41}$.

*6. Make up a sequence of rationals which has an irrational number as its limit.

5–4 LIMITS OF FUNCTIONS DEFINED ON THE REAL NUMBERS

Definition 5–4.1. If a and b are real numbers, $a < b$, the set

$$\{x \mid a < x \wedge x < b\},$$

is called the *open interval* from a to b, written $]a, b[$.

Definition 5–4.2. If a and b are real numbers, $a < b$, the set

$$\{x \mid a \leq x \wedge x \leq b\},$$

is called the *closed interval* from a to b, written $[a, b]$.

If we want to include the point a but not b, we write $[a, b[$; or if we want to include b but not a, we write $]a, b]$. Such intervals are neither open nor closed.

EXAMPLE 5–4.1. Find the solution set to the open sentence $0 \leq x \leq 2$. Answer: $[0, 2]$.

EXAMPLE 5–4.2. Find the solution set for the open sentence $|x - 1| < 2$. By definition,

$$|x - 1| = \begin{cases} x - 1 \text{ if } x - 1 \geq 0, \\ -(x - 1) \text{ if } x - 1 < 0. \end{cases}$$

The solution set of the given open sentence is the same as the solution set of the sentence

$$(x - 1 < 2 \wedge x - 1 \geq 0) \vee (-(x - 1) < 2 \wedge x - 1 < 0).$$

This, in turn, may be written

$$(x < 3 \wedge x \geq 1) \vee (x > -1 \wedge x < 1).$$

The solution set is the union of the sets $[1, 3[$ and $]-1, 1[$;

$$[1, 3[\cup]-1, 1[=]-1, 3[.$$

The solution set is also $\{x \mid$ the distance of x from 1 is less than 2$\}$.

Some geometric pictures may help to clarify the definitions. The solution sets for Examples 5–4.1 and 5–4.2 are given in Fig. 5–2.

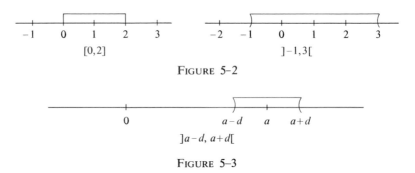

FIGURE 5-2

FIGURE 5-3

In general, the solution set for the open sentence $|x - a| < d$ is $]a - d, a + d[$ if $d > 0$. Geometrically, the open sentence states that the distance of x from a is less than d. (See Fig. 5–3.)

With these preliminaries out of the way, we are now in a position to talk about the limit of a function at a point. Suppose that the function f is defined by $y = f(x)$. If the domain of f contains some open interval about the point $x = a$, then we say that $\lim_{x \to a} f(x) = L$ [read limit of $f(x)$ as x approaches a is L] means that $f(x)$ is as close to L as we please, provided that x is close enough to a.

> EXAMPLE 5–4.3. If $f(x) = x + 2$, $\lim_{x \to 0} f(x) = 2$. This simply says that we may find values of $x + 2$ as close to 2 as we please, provided that a value of x is taken close enough to 0.

We proceed to state precisely what "as close as we please" and "close enough" mean.

Definition 5–4.3. If $f(x)$ is defined at every point in an open interval containing a, except perhaps at $x = a$ itself, then given any $\epsilon > 0$, if there exists $\delta > 0$ such that $|f(x) - L| < \epsilon$, provided that $0 < |x - a| < \delta$, we say that $\lim_{x \to a} f(x) = L$.

The ϵ specifies how close we wish $f(x)$ to be to L and the δ tells us how close we must take x to a in order to ensure this degree of closeness.

Geometrically, this definition means that if we sketch the graphs of f and L, then if we are given a small number ϵ, we must be able to determine a real number $\delta > 0$ such that when x is in an interval of width 2δ centered on a, the corresponding value of $f(x)$ will lie in a strip of width 2ϵ centered on the line L.

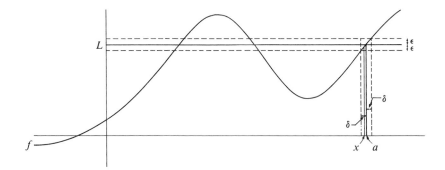

You will note in the definition that not only is $|x - a| < \delta$ but $0 < |x - a|$. This latter condition emphasizes the fact that the situation at $x = a$ is irrelevant for the existence of the limit of $f(x)$ at the point $x = a$.

Definition 5–4.4. If $\lim_{x \to a} f(x) = f(a)$, we say that f is continuous at the point $x = a$. If a function is continuous at every point in an interval, it is said to be *continuous in the interval*.

Intuitively, we think of a continuous curve as an unbroken curve, and the above definition makes precise this notation for a curve that is continuous in an interval. Most of the functions which we encountered in Chapter 4 were continuous almost everywhere. All constant functions, all linear functions, and all polynomials are continuous everywhere. Even rational functions (quotients of polynomials) are continuous at every point in the domain of the function.

The greatest integer function $f = \{(x,[x])\}$ of Example 4–4.5 is an example of a function which is not continuous at any integer but is continuous at every other real number. However, the definition of continuity at a point extends the intuitive notion of an unbroken curve to include much more complicated behavior for functions.

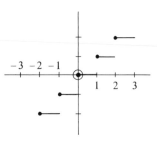

EXAMPLE 5–4.4

$$f(x) = \begin{cases} 0 \text{ for } x \text{ irrational,} \\ 1/n \text{ for } x = m/n, \ m \text{ and } n \text{ integers } n \neq 0, \\ \quad m \text{ and } n \text{ have no common factors.} \end{cases}$$

This function, by our definition, is continuous at every irrational number x and discontinuous at every rational number.

EXAMPLE 5–4.5

$$f(x) = \begin{cases} 0 \text{ for } x \text{ irrational,} \\ 1 \text{ for } x \text{ rational.} \end{cases}$$

This function, on the other hand, is not continuous for any real number x.

Neither of the functions in Examples 5–4.4 and 5–4.5 is continuous in any interval and, accordingly, the graphs of these functions consist entirely of disconnected points.

EXERCISES

1. Find the sets defined by the following:
   (a) $[1, 2] \cup [2, 3]$.   (b) $[1, 4] \cap]3, 6]$.   (c) $[1, 4] \cap]4, 5[$.
   (d) $[0, 1] \cap]\frac{1}{2}, 2]$.   (e) $|x - 1| = 2$.   (f) $|x - 1| < 1$.
   (g) $|x - 2| \geq 2$. [*Hint:* Use $\bar{A}$, the complement of A.]
   (h) $|x - a| \leq 4$.   (i) $x - 1 \geq 0 \wedge x - 2 \leq 3$.

2. Find the following limits:
   (a) $\lim_{x \to 0} |x|$.
   (b) $\lim_{x \to 1} x/x^2$.

(c) $\lim\limits_{x \to 1} |-x - 1|$.

(d) $\lim\limits_{x \to 1} (2x + 2)$.

(e) $\lim\limits_{x \to 0} (2x^2 - 2x - 1)$.

(f) $\lim\limits_{x \to 2} \dfrac{x^2 - 4}{x - 2}$.

3. Which of the following functions are continuous at $x = 1$? Justify your answer.

(a) $f = \{(x, x + 1)\}$.

(b) $f = \{(x, y) \mid y = x - 1\}$.

(c) $f = \left\{(x, y) \mid y = \dfrac{x^2 - 1}{x + 1}\right\}$.

(d) $f = \left\{(x, y) \mid y = \dfrac{x^2 - 1}{x - 1}\right\}$.

(e) $f = \left\{(x, y) \mid y = \dfrac{1}{x - 1}\right\}$.

4. If $f(x) = x^2$, find $\lim\limits_{h \to 0} \dfrac{f(x + h) - f(x)}{h}$.

*5. If $f(x) = |x|$, find $\lim\limits_{h \to 0} \dfrac{f(x + h) - f(x)}{h}$.

*6. Given $f(x) = x^2 + 1$, prove that $\lim\limits_{x \to 0} f(x) = 1$. [*Hint:* Given $\epsilon > 0$, find δ in terms of ϵ so that $|f(x) - 1| < \epsilon$ if $0 < |x - 0| < \delta$.]

*7. If $f(x) = x^2 + 1$, illustrate geometrically the definitions of $\lim\limits_{x \to 0} f(x)$.

*8. Using Definition 5–4.3, show that the function defined in Example 5–4.4 is continuous at any irrational number x.

*9. Give an argument to show that the function in Example 5–4.4 is not continuous at any rational number x.

*10. Show that the function of Example 5–4.5 is not continuous at any real number x.

11. Show that $\lim\limits_{x \to a} c \cdot f(x) = c \cdot \lim\limits_{x \to a} f(x)$.

12. Show that $\lim\limits_{x \to a} (f(x) + g(x)) = \lim\limits_{x \to a} f(x) + \lim\limits_{x \to a} g(x)$.

*13. Show that $\lim\limits_{x \to a} f(x) \cdot g(x) = \lim\limits_{x \to a} f(x) \cdot \lim\limits_{x \to a} g(x)$.

REVIEW EXERCISES

1. The sequence $s_n = (1 + 1/n)^n$ converges to the number e, the base of the system of natural logarithms. Find the first four terms of this sequence.

2. Which of the following sequences are divergent?

(a) $\{(n, s_n) \mid s_n = 2^n\}$.

(b) $\{(n, s_n) \mid s_n = 1 + 1/2n\}$.

(c) $\{(n, s_n) \mid s_n = 1 + (-2)^n\}$.

(d) $\{(n, s_n) \mid s_n = 5n/(n^2 + 1)\}$.

3. Decide whether or not the sequence converges. If it converges, find the limit.

(a) $s_n = 1/2^n$.   (b) $s_n = 1 + (-1)^n/2^n$.   (c) $s_n = 3 - 1/n$.
(d) $s_n = (-1)^n/n$.   (e) $s_n = n^2$.   (f) $s_n = (-1)^n$.
(g) $s_n = 2 + 3/n^2$.

4. Find the following limits:

(a) $\lim_{x \to 2} (x^2 - 3)$.

(b) $\lim_{x \to 3} \dfrac{x^2 - 9}{x - 3}$.

(c) $\lim_{x \to 1} (x^2 + 1)$.

(d) $\lim_{h \to 0} (3x^2 + 2hx + h^2)$.

(e) $\lim_{h \to 1} (h^2 + 3h)$.

(f) $\lim_{h \to 0} \dfrac{(x + h)^2 - x^2}{h}$.

5. Write $\frac{7}{13}$ as a repeating decimal.

6. Find the rational number whose decimal expansion is $3.1\overline{23}$.

7. If f is continuous at $x = a$, what is the $\lim_{x \to a} f(x)$?

8. (a) What is the geometric interpretation of the open sentence $|x - \frac{1}{2}| < 2$?

(b) What is the solution set of the open sentence in (a)?

9. Explain the meaning of each of the following, and illustrate with an example.

(a) $\lim_{n \to \infty} s_n = s$.   (b) $\lim_{x \to a} f(x) = L$.

10. Give an example of a function which is not continuous at a point.

Suggested Readings

ALLENDOERFER and OAKLEY, *Principles of Mathematics*, second edition, McGraw-Hill, New York, 1963, Ch. 10, pp. 320–354.

*KRAMER, E., *The Main Stream of Mathematics*, Oxford University Press, New York, 1951 (Fibonacci Sequence), pp. 40–42.

*NORTHROP, E. P., *Riddles in Mathematics*, Van Nostrand, Princeton, 1944 (The Fibonacci Series), pp. 48–55.

*RICHARDSON, M., *Fundamentals of Mathematics*, Macmillan, New York, 1958, Ch. 11, pp. 299–308.

TITCHMARSH, E. C., *Mathematics for the General Reader*, Doubleday Anchor Books, Garden City, N. Y., 1959, Chs. 8 and 9, pp. 90–115.

General References

COURANT and ROBBINS, *What Is Mathematics?*, Oxford University Press, New York, 1941.

NCTM Twenty-third Yearbook, *Insights into Modern Mathematics*, "Limits" by John F. Randolph, NCTM, Washington, 1957, pp. 200–226.

VOROB'EV, N. N., *Fibonacci Numbers*, Blaisdell Publishing Company, New York, 1961.

6 | THE CALCULUS

6–1 INTRODUCTION

In the last chapter we introduced one of the most difficult and enduring achievements of mathematics, the precise formulation of the idea of a limit. The exploitation of this idea is the chief concern of the branch of mathematics called analysis. In this part of mathematics, we are primarily concerned with problems involving limits of functions.

We shall devote this chapter to a brief look at one of the most powerful weapons in the mathematics arsenal, the calculus. It uses the idea of a limit to solve two important problems which, in turn, have been recast so as to apply to innumerable problems encountered in the physical world. In fact, the calculus is probably the most useful tool yet devised for formulating and solving scientific problems.

6–2 THE PROBLEM OF TANGENTS

Suppose that in the not-too-distant future, a famous author is traveling on an automatic highway. The electronic brain driving his car fails. Unfortunately, the highway at this point parallels a rather deep mountain lake into which the car vanishes. Luckily, the author is an excellent swimmer; however, in his haste to escape from the sinking car, he abandons the manuscript of his latest novel, which is locked in a waterproof box in the trunk of the car.

The state highway patrol officer monitoring traffic on the superhighway marked the spot at which the vehicle left the highway. A skin diver with a partner who knows a good deal about mathematics is immediately rushed to the scene. The pair make some observations and a few calculations. The diver hops in, swims several hundred feet, checks with his partner on the bank, and goes down to retrieve the manuscript. The literary world sighs with relief!

The spot where the car lies depends, of course, on several factors, all of which were considered by the diver's mathematically literate friend in determining the place to dive. One of the most important factors was the direction in which the car left the superhighway.

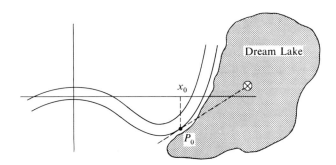

Suppose that we neglect all the factors such as wind, condition of the shoulders, depth of the water, currents, etc., and concentrate only on the direction which the car took as it left the highway. The car will move along the tangent to the curve at the point where the car left the road. The problem of determining the tangent to a curve is precisely the problem we wish to consider in this section.

Suppose that the highway near the point in question follows the graph of a function defined by $y = f(x)$. The car leaves the highway at point P_0. What is the tangent to the curve at this point?

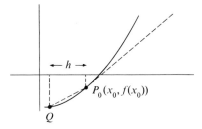

We know that the *tangent to a circle* is a line which touches the circle in exactly one point. One of the theorems of plane geometry states that the tangent to a circle at a point is perpendicular to the radius drawn to that point. However, for the curve above, this information is of no help.

However, suppose that we consider chords 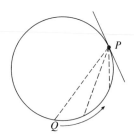 $\overline{PQ}$ on the circle passing through the point P. The tangent at P might be thought of as the limiting position of the chord $\overline{PQ}$ as Q approaches P. This idea carries over to other curves with no difficulty whatever. To determine which line is actually the tangent, we need only find the slope of the line which is the limiting position of the secant line $\overline{PQ}$.

Presumably, the abscissa of the point Q as Q approaches P_0 on the curve differs from x_0 by only a small amount, say h. Then we may designate Q as the point with coordinates $(x_0 + h, f(x_0 + h))$. The slope of $\overline{PQ}$ is

$$\frac{f(x_0 + h) - f(x_0)}{(x_0 + h) - x_0} = \frac{f(x_0 + h) - f(x_0)}{h}.$$

If this expression involving the variable h has a limit as $h \to 0$, that certainly should be the slope of the limiting position of $\overline{PQ}$ as Q approaches P on the curve. Accordingly, we make the following definition.

Definition 6–2.1. The *tangent to the curve*, which is the graph of the function f, *at the point* $P_0(x_0, f(x_0))$, is the line passing through P_0 with slope

$$\lim_{h \to 0} \frac{f(x_0 + h) - f(x_0)}{h}.$$

Definition 6–2.2. The *derivative* of the function f is the function Df which has the slope of the tangent to the curve $y = f(x)$ as its value at x; that is,

$$Df = \left\{ (x, y) \mid y = \lim_{h \to 0} \frac{f(x + h) - f(x)}{h} \right\}.$$

Df is frequently written f', and then

$$f'(x) = \lim_{h \to 0} \frac{f(x + h) - f(x)}{h}.$$

Thus the tangent to a curve at a point can be determined if we know the function f, which has the curve as its graph, and the value of the derivative of the function at the point.

EXAMPLE 6-2.1. Find the tangent to the curve given by $y = x^2$ at the point $(2, 4)$.

Solution. The tangent is the line passing through $(2, 4)$ with slope $m = f'(2)$. For $x_0 = 2$,

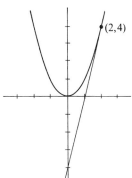

$$f'(x_0) = \lim_{h \to 0} \frac{f(x_0 + h) - f(x_0)}{h}$$

$$= \lim_{h \to 0} \frac{(2 + h)^2 - 2^2}{h}$$

$$= \lim_{h \to 0} \frac{4h + h^2}{h}$$

$$= \lim_{h \to 0} (4 + h) = 4.$$

Therefore, the tangent is the line passing through the point $(2, 4)$ with slope 4. It is the graph of the function defined by $y = 4x + b$. But if the line passes through $(2, 4)$, $4 = 8 + b$, or $b = -4$. Therefore, the tangent is the line which is the graph of $\{(x, y) \mid y = 4x - 4\}$.

EXAMPLE 6-2.2. Find the tangent to $f = \{(x, 2x^2 + x - 1)\}$ at $(0, -1)$.

$$f(x) = 2x^2 + x - 1.$$

$$f'(x) = \lim_{h \to 0} \frac{f(x + h) - f(x)}{h}$$

$$= \lim_{h \to 0} \frac{2(x + h)^2 + (x + h) - 1 - (2x^2 + x - 1)}{h}$$

$$= \lim_{h \to 0} \frac{4hx + 2h^2 + h}{h}$$

$$= \lim_{h \to 0} (2h + 4x + 1)$$

$$= 4x + 1.$$

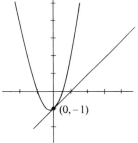

Therefore, the tangent is the line through $(0, -1)$ with slope 1.

If $y = 1(x) + b$ passes through $(0, -1)$, then $-1 = b$, and the tangent is the graph of $\{(x, y) \mid y = x - 1\}$.

The new function Df, determined from the given function f by the process of finding a limit, proves to have far wider applications than merely determining tangents to curves. We shall consider some of these in the next section.

EXERCISES

For Exercises 1 through 12, determine the derivative of the functions defined by:

1. $f(x) = 2$.
2. $f(x) = c$.
3. $f(x) = x$.
4. $f(x) = mx$.
5. $f(x) = 2x + 3$.
6. $f(x) = mx + b$.
7. $f(x) = ax^2$.
8. $f(x) = x^3$.
9. $f(x) = 4x^2 + 5x + 6$.
*10. $f(x) = |x|$.
*11. $f(x) = [x]$.
*12. $f(x) = x^n$.

13. Find the tangent to the curve given by $f(x) = 3x^2 - 1$ at the point $(1, 2)$. Sketch the graph of the curve and the tangent.

14. Find the tangent to the curve given by $f(x) = 3x^2$ at $(1, 3)$. Sketch the graph of f and its tangent at $(1, 3)$.

15. Find the derivative of the derivative of $f = \{(x, \frac{1}{3}x^3)\}$.

*16. What is the slope of the tangent to $f = \{(x, |x|)\}$ at $(0, 0)$?

+17. Show that $D(cf) = c \cdot Df$ if c is a constant function.

+18. Show that $D(f + g) = Df + Dg$ for any functions f and g which have derivatives.

+19. Show that $D(f - g) = Df - Dg$.

+*20. Show that $D(fg) \neq (Df) \cdot (Dg)$.

6–3 THE DERIVATIVE

A space capsule leaves the launching pad at 7:03 a.m. The time of impact 300 miles down range is 7:18 a.m. How fast did the capsule travel? In an attempt to solve this problem, we might determine the time of the flight and divide the distance traveled by the time it took to go that distance; $d/t = 300/15 = 20$ miles per minute, or 1200 miles per hour (mph). We would then say that the average speed for this 15-minute flight was 1200 mph. During the few minutes when the astronaut was in space, suppose that he looked at his instruments and found that he was traveling at the rate of 1500 .mph. What would this mean? At the instant he consulted his instruments, he certainly did not go 1500 miles; in fact, he did not travel 1500 miles on the entire trip. The distance traveled during zero minutes should surely be zero miles. What, then, does it mean to say that his speed at that instant was 1500 mph? Perhaps during the previous minute he had traveled 25 miles; and if he continued to travel at that rate for 59 more minutes, he would have gone 1500 miles in an hour. However, in the next minute his speed may have been only 1000 mph. Although the meaning of the statement, the average speed over a certain time interval is v mph (distance/time $= v$), may be clear, just exactly what is meant by saying the speed at some instant is v_0 mph is less clear.

If we try to give this notion a precise definition, we are led to consider a rather familiar-looking expression. Suppose that s is the distance traveled in t minutes. We are really dealing with a function

$$s = \{(t, s(t)) \mid s(t) \text{ is the distance traveled in } t \text{ minutes}\}.$$

The domain of the function is a set whose members are time intervals measured in minutes; while the range is a set of distances measured in miles.

The average speed over the time interval $[t_0, t_0 + h]$ is

$$\frac{s(t_0 + h) - s(t_0)}{(t_0 + h) - t_0} = \frac{s(t_0 + h) - s(t_0)}{h}.$$

If we take smaller and smaller values for h, we should get better and better approximations as to what we would like to mean by the speed at the time t_0. But this is exactly the process we use to find the value of the derivative of the function s at the point t_0.

We therefore define the *instantaneous speed* at time t_0 to be

$$s'(t_0) = \lim_{h \to 0} \frac{s(t_0 + h) - s(t_0)}{h}.$$

For any particular value of h, the quotient $[s(t_0 + h) - s(t_0)]/h$ gives the average speed over the time interval $[t_0, t_0 + h]$, and this average is the difference in distance divided by the difference in time measured from some fixed starting point. We say that such a quotient gives the *average rate of change of distance with respect to time*.

In many other situations, the independent and dependent variables of a function stand for physical quantities, and we are frequently interested in the rate of change of one variable with respect to another. If $f = \{(x, y) \mid y = f(x)\}$ instead of

$$\lim_{h \to 0} \frac{f(x + h) - f(x)}{x + h - x},$$

we often find the notation $\lim_{\Delta x \to 0} (\Delta y/\Delta x)$, where the symbols Δx and Δy (Δ is the Greek letter delta) stand for the differences between the two values of x and of y, respectively. These differences,

$$\Delta x = x + h - x = h$$

and

$$\Delta y = f(x + h) - f(x),$$

are called *increments*.

To serve as a reminder that the derivative is the limit of the quotient of these differences (that is, it is the rate of change of y with respect to x), the derivative is often written

$$\frac{dy}{dx} = \lim_{\Delta x \to 0} \frac{\Delta y}{\Delta x} = \lim_{h \to 0} \frac{f(x + h) - f(x)}{h}.$$

We shall not use this notation, since dy/dx is simply another symbol for $Df(x)$ or $f'(x)$, and its form suggests that the derivative is a quotient, rather than the limit of a quotient.

> EXAMPLE 6–3.1. A firm handling sugar can sell x pounds of sugar per month at a price of y cents a pound, where
>
> $$y = 10 - x/8000.$$
>
> The total monthly revenue is then
>
> $$R = xy = 10x - x^2/8000.$$
>
> The rate of change of R with respect to x is called the *marginal revenue* at the output x. In economic theory, marginal revenue is an important concept. Find the marginal revenue for an arbitrary output x, and find its value for outputs of 10, 20, and 25 tons a month.
>
> *Solution.* The equation for the monthly revenue,
>
> $$R = 10x - \frac{x^2}{8000} \text{ cents,}$$

determines the revenue function $R = \{(x, 10x - x^2/8000)\}$. The derivative of this function gives the marginal revenue, the rate of change in monthly revenue with respect to the change in output.

$$R'(x) = \lim_{\Delta x \to 0} \frac{\Delta R}{\Delta x} = \lim_{h \to 0} \frac{R(x + h) - R(x)}{h}$$

$$= \lim_{h \to 0} \frac{10(x + h) - (x + h)^2/8000 - (10x - x^2/8000)}{h}$$

$$= \lim_{h \to 0} \frac{(10h - 2hx/8000 - h^2/8000)}{h}$$

$$= \lim_{h \to 0} \left(10 - \frac{2x}{8000} - \frac{h}{8000}\right)$$

$$= 10 - \frac{2x}{8000} = 10 - \frac{x}{4000};$$

$$R'(20,000) = 10 - \frac{20,000}{4000} = 5 \text{ cents/pound}$$

$$(10 \text{ tons} = 20,000 \text{ pounds}),$$

$$R'(40,000) = 10 - \frac{40,000}{4000} = 0 \text{ cents/pound}$$

$$(20 \text{ tons} = 40,000 \text{ pounds}),$$

$$R'(50,000) = 10 - \frac{50,000}{4000} = -2\tfrac{1}{2} \text{ cents/pound}$$

$$(25 \text{ tons} = 50,000 \text{ pounds}).$$

Of course, to determine the most profitable level of operation for the firm, one must consider not only the rate of change of revenue with respect to output, but also the rate of change of cost of production with respect to output and the output itself.

EXERCISES

1. A freely falling body falls a distance $s = 16t^2$ feet in t seconds. Find the speed (velocity) of the falling body at time $t = 0$; at $t = 2$.

2. The rate of change of velocity with respect to time is called *acceleration*. Find the acceleration of the falling body of Exercise 1 at $t = 0$; at $t = 2$.

3. Suppose that the body in Exercise 1 is dropped from a height of 60 feet. When will it hit the ground? What is the velocity (speed) at the time it hits the ground?

4. In each of the following, find the rate of change of y with respect to x; discuss the meaning of the rate of change in each.

	y		x
		y	x
(a)	$y = 32x$	Speed	Time
(b)	$y = 16x^2$	Distance traveled	Gallons of fuel used
(c)	$y = \pi x^2$	Area of a circle	Radius
(d)	$y = 2\pi x$	Circumference of a circle	Radius
(e)	$y = 3x$	Problems solved	Time in hours

5. If a hemispherical bowl of radius 10 inches is filled with water to a depth of x inches, the volume of water is given by $V = \pi(10 - x/3)x^2$. Find the rate of increase of the volume per inch increase in the depth.

6. A bus will hold 60 people. If the number x of persons per trip who use the bus is related to the fare charged (p nickels) by the equation $p = (3 - x/40)^2$, what is the function expressing the total revenue per trip received by the bus company? What is the number of people per trip which will make the marginal revenue zero? What is the corresponding fare?

6-4 APPLICATIONS TO CURVE TRACING

The limit which we considered in determining the tangent to a curve and the rate of change of one variable with respect to another is extremely useful in obtaining information about the graph of a function.

EXAMPLE 6–4.1. Sketch the graph of the quadratic function $f = \{(x, x^2 - x - 6)\}$. We have already indicated that the value of the derivative $f'(x)$ gives the slope of the tangent to the curve at the point $(x, f(x))$. For this particular function,

$$f'(x) = \lim_{h \to 0} \frac{f(x + h) - f(x)}{h}$$

$$= \lim_{h \to 0} \frac{(x + h)^2 - (x + h) - 6 - (x^2 - x - 6)}{h}$$

$$= \lim_{h \to 0} \frac{2hx + h^2 - h}{h} = \lim_{h \to 0} (2x - 1 + h) = 2x - 1.$$

In the last section, we noted that $f'(x) = \lim_{\Delta x \to 0} (\Delta y / \Delta x)$. The value of $f'(x)$ at $(x, f(x))$ gives us a very good idea about how the curve is changing near that point. For, if Δx is small, $(\Delta y / \Delta x)$ is close to $f'(x)$ [that is what it means to say that $\lim_{\Delta x \to 0} (\Delta y / \Delta x) = f'(x)$]. Hence near $(1, -6)$, Δy is close to Δx, while near $(2, -4)$, Δy is about $3\Delta x$; that is, near $(1, -6)$, x and y are changing at the same rate, but near $(2, -4)$, y is changing three times as fast as x. If we take Δx to be small and positive near $x = 1$, then the increment Δy is about the same as Δx. Therefore, starting at $(1, -6)$ to find a point on the curve, we could go to the right the amount Δx and up about the same amount; while if we started at $(2, -4)$, we would go to the right Δx and up about three times as far to reach a point on the curve. Both of these operations suggest that the curve is going up near $(1, -6)$ and $(2, -4)$ and that the rate at which it is increasing at $(2, -4)$ is about three times that at $(1, -6)$. In fact, whenever $f'(x) = \lim_{\Delta x \to 0} (\Delta y / \Delta x) > 0$, if we take Δx positive, Δy will be positive also, and the curve must be going up, i.e., *increasing*. On the other hand, at the point where $f'(x) = \lim_{\Delta x \to 0} (\Delta y / \Delta x) < 0$, if we take Δx small and positive, then Δy will be negative. And to reach a nearby point on the curve, we go to the right and down. In this case we say that the curve is *decreasing*. At $(\tfrac{1}{2}, -6\tfrac{1}{4})$, $f'(\tfrac{1}{2}) = 0$, and geometrically this would indicate that near this point the curve is stationary; that is, it ceases going down and has not begun to go up. The tangent here is horizontal.

We can look at the derivative f', then, and gather the following geometric information about the graph of f.

1. If $f'(x) > 0$, $y = f(x)$ is increasing near the point $(x, f(x))$ as we go from left to right.

2. If $f'(x) < 0$, $y = f(x)$ is decreasing near the point $(x, f(x))$ as we go from left to right.

3. If $f'(x) = 0$,   the curve is stationary at $(x, f(x))$.

In Fig. 6-6 we have drawn very small segments of the tangent line at the points plotted on the curve. These tell us the direction of the graph at these points and give us a very good idea about how to sketch the graph.

If we look again at $f'(x) = 2x - 1$, we see that

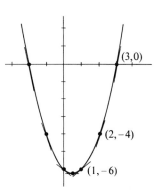

$$f'(x) = 2x - 1 > 0 \qquad \text{for} \qquad x > \tfrac{1}{2}$$
$$< 0 \qquad \text{for} \qquad x < \tfrac{1}{2}$$
$$= 0 \qquad \text{for} \qquad x = \tfrac{1}{2}.$$

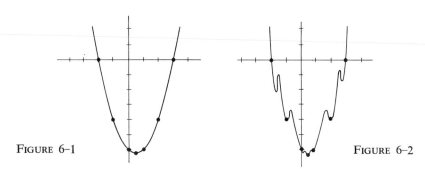

FIGURE 6–1

FIGURE 6–2

The graph of f thus decreases for all values of $x < \frac{1}{2}$, and increases for all values of $x > \frac{1}{2}$. Consequently, we connect the points by a smooth curve, as in Fig. 6–1, and not by a wavering graph, as in Fig. 6–2.

The points on the graph at which the derivative is zero are particularly significant for drawing the graph, since these are the stationary points where the curve is neither increasing nor decreasing. It may be that on one side of such a point the curve was decreasing, while on the other side it was increasing. Such a point is called a *relative maximum* or a *relative minimum*, depending on whether the curve increases on the left and decreases on the right or decreases on the left and increases on the right.

We have the following procedure for determining relative maximum and relative minimum points.

1. Locate the points $(a, f(a))$ at which $f'(a) = 0$.
2. If $f'(a - h) > 0$ and $f'(a + h) < 0$ (h is small and positive), then $(a, f(a))$ is a maximum point.
3. If $f'(a - h) < 0$ and $f'(a + h) > 0$, then $(a, f(a))$ is a minimum point.

Of course it may happen that $f'(a) = 0$, and neither of the conditions 2 or 3 is satisfied.

EXAMPLE 6–4.2

$$f = \{(x, x^3)\}.$$

$$f'(x) = \lim_{h \to 0} \frac{(x + h)^3 - x^3}{h} = \lim_{h \to 0} \frac{3hx^2 + 3h^2x + h^3}{h}$$

$$= \lim_{h \to 0} (3x^2 + 3hx + h^2) = 3x^2.$$

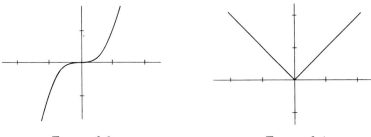

FIGURE 6-3   FIGURE 6-4

Then $f'(0) = 0$, but $f'(-h) = f'(h) = 3h^2 > 0$. In such a case the curve merely stops increasing for a moment and then resumes its upward way. The tangent at $(0, 0)$ is horizontal and *crosses* the curve there.

It may also happen that we have a relative maximum or relative minimum at a point $(a, f(a))$ at which $f'(a) \neq 0$; for example, $f = \{(x, |x|)\}$ at $(0, 0)$. (See Fig. 6-4.) In this case the minimum occurs at the origin, but the derivative does not exist there.

We have used the terms relative maximum and relative minimum because these points are the highest and lowest among those nearby points on the graph of the function. These need not give the greatest nor the least values that the function may have.

EXAMPLE 6-4.3

$$f = \{(x, x^3 - 3x)\}.$$

$$f'(x) = \lim_{h \to 0} \frac{(x + h)^3 - 3(x + h) - (x^3 - 3x)}{h}$$

$$= \lim_{h \to 0} \frac{3hx^2 + 3h^2x + h^3 - 3h}{h}$$

$$= \lim_{h \to 0} (3x^2 + 3hx + h^2 - 3)$$

$$= 3x^2 - 3.$$

Thus $f'(1) = f'(-1) = 0$, and $(1, -2)$ is a relative minimum and $(-1, 2)$ is a relative maximum. However there are values of f which are greater than 2 and less than -2; for example, $f(3) = 18$ and $f(-3) = -18$.

It may happen that if the domain of the function is restricted, say to a closed interval, then the maximum or minimum values may occur at an end point of the interval where the derivative is not zero; for example, if $f = \{(x, |x|) \mid |x| \leq 1\}$, then $(1, 1)$ and $(-1, 1)$ are maximum values of f, but not relative maxima as we are using the term.

To sum up, the graph of f is increasing when f' is positive and decreasing when f' is negative. Relative maximum and minimum points may occur either where $f'(x) = 0$ or where f' fails to exist. Maximum and minimum points occur either at relative maximum and minimum points or at the end points of an interval.

If we apply these results to the derivative function f', f' is increasing where $Df' = f'' > 0$, and f' is decreasing where $f'' < 0$. Therefore, since at a relative maximum point $(a, f(a))$, if f' exists, $f'(a - h) > 0$, $f'(a) = 0$, $f'(a + h) < 0$, the values of the function f' go from positive through zero to negative; that is, f' itself is decreasing. Accordingly, if $f''(a) < 0$, and $f'(a) = 0$, then $(a, f(a))$ is a relative maximum. Similarly, if $f''(a) > 0$ and $f'(a) = 0$, then $(a, f(a))$ is a relative minimum. (These conditions are sufficient but not necessary, since $f = \{(x, x^4)\}$ has $f'(0) = 0$ and $f''(0) = 0$, yet $(0, 0)$ is a relative minimum.)

$f'' < 0$ $f'' > 0$

Concave downward   Concave upward

The curve which is the graph of f is said to be *concave upward* in an interval in which f'' is positive, since a chord joining two points on the graph in this interval lies above the curve; on the other hand, in an interval in which f'' is negative, a similar chord lies below the curve, and in this case we say that the curve is *concave downward*.

EXERCISES

For Exercises 1 through 8, find the maxima and the minima, and sketch the graph of the function. Find the interval in which the function is concave upward, concave downward.

1. $\{(x, y) \mid y = x^2 - 1\}$.
2. $\{(x, y) \mid y = x^2 - 4x + 3\}$.
3. $\{(x, y) \mid y = x^4 - x^2\}$.
4. $\{(x, y) \mid y = 4x - x^2 + 3\}$.

5. $\{(x, y) \mid y = 4x - x^3\}$.

6. $\{(x, y) \mid y = x^3 - 6x^2 + 12x - 8\}$.

7. $\{(x, y) \mid y = 12 - 12x + x^3\}$.

8. $\{(x, y) \mid y = x^3 \wedge |x| \leq 1\}$.

9. A rectangular field is to be enclosed by 100 feet of fence. Find the dimensions of the rectangle if the area is to be as large as possible. [*Hint:* Let x be the length and $50 - x$ be the width.]

10. Suppose that the amount of fence in Exercise 9 had been 200 feet. What should the dimensions of the rectangle be if the area enclosed is to be as large as possible?

11. On the basis of Exercises 9 and 10, what would you conjecture about the length and width of the rectangle enclosing the maximum area for any fixed amount of fence? Try to prove your conjecture.

12. A projectile shot straight up from a height of 6 feet has an initial velocity of 192 feet per second. Its height after t seconds is given by $h = 6 + 192t - 16t^2$, where h is measured in feet. After how many seconds does the projectile reach its maximum height? What is that maximum?

13. A telephone company can get 1000 subscribers at a monthly rate of 5 dollars each. It will get 100 more subscribers for each 10-cent decrease in the rate. What rate will yield the maximum gross monthly income, and what is this income?

14. An open rectangular box is to be made from a piece of cardboard 8 inches wide and 15 inches long by cutting a square from each corner and bending up the sides. Find the dimensions of the box of largest volume.

6–5 AREA

The geometrical problem of constructing the tangent to a curve led us to formulate a limit (the derivative) which gave us the slope of the tangent to a curve. The problem of determining the area enclosed by a curved line leads us to the second important limit in the calculus.

We begin again with a circle. Suppose that we wish to find the area of a circle with radius 1. The area of a rectangle is the length of the base b times the altitude a. The area of the circle ought to be greater than the area of the inscribed square (diagonal of length 2 and side $\sqrt{2}$) but less than the area of the circumscribed square (length of side 2).

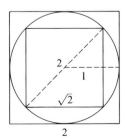

Therefore, $(\sqrt{2})^2 <$ area of the circle $< 2^2$, or $2 <$ area of the circle < 4.

A better approximation would be obtained by increasing the number of sides of the inscribed and circumscribed regular polygons. It is clear that the area of the circle would always be between the values A_{I_n} and A_{C_n}, the respective areas of the inscribed and circumscribed regular polygons with 2^{n+1} sides.

Consequently, $A_{I_n} <$ area of the circle $< A_{C_n}$ for all positive integers n. Now if it could be shown that $\lim_{n \to \infty} (A_{C_n} - A_{I_n}) = 0$, then

$$\lim_{n \to \infty} A_{C_n} = \lim_{n \to \infty} A_{I_n} = \text{area of the circle} = \pi.$$

This limiting process furnishes us with a reasonable and precise way of saying what we mean by the area enclosed by this particular curved line.

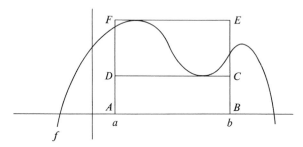

Suppose that we take f to be a function which is positive and continuous in the interval $[a, b]$. We would like to say precisely what we mean by the area under the curve f in the interval $[a, b]$. Whatever that area is, it is clear that it is greater than the area of the "inscribed rectangle" $ABCD$ and less than that of the "circumscribed rectangle" $ABEF$. Rather than increase the number of sides of the inscribed and circumscribed polygons, we approximate the area by several rectangles with smaller and smaller bases. In fact, we divide the interval $[a, b]$ of length $b - a$ into n equal subintervals, each of length $(b - a)/n$. In each of these subintervals, we approximate the area under the curve by inscribed and circumscribed rectangles. Then the area under the curve in the interval $[a, b]$ is approximated by the following sums:

$$\underline{S_n} = f(x_{1_m}) \frac{b - a}{n} + f(x_{2_m}) \frac{b - a}{n} + \cdots + f(x_{n_m}) \frac{b - a}{n},$$

where $f(x_{i_m})$ is the value of the function f, which gives the height of the ith inscribed rectangle ($i = 1, 2, \ldots, n$), and

$$\overline{S}_n = f(x_{1_M})\frac{b-a}{n} + f(x_{2_M})\frac{b-a}{n} + \cdots + f(x_{n_M})\frac{b-a}{n},$$

where $f(x_{i_M})$ is the value of the function f which gives the height of the ith circumscribed rectangle ($i = 1, 2, \ldots, n$).†

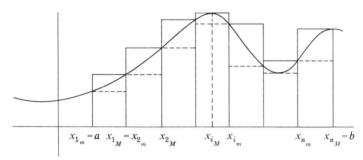

There is a convenient space-saving notation for sums which we shall use in the remainder of this chapter. The two sums above may be written

$$\underline{S}_n = \sum_{i=1}^{n} f(x_{i_m})\frac{b-a}{n} \quad \text{and} \quad \overline{S}_n = \sum_{i=1}^{n} f(x_{i_M})\frac{b-a}{n}.$$

The symbol $\sum$ is the Greek capital letter sigma and is an appropriate notation to use for a sum. In general, $\sum_{i=1}^{n} a_i = a_1 + a_2 + \cdots + a_n$.

The number A, which we would like to call the area, is always between $\underline{S}_n$ and $\overline{S}_n$; that is, $\underline{S}_n \leq A \leq \overline{S}_n$ for all natural numbers n. Now, if we let n get larger and larger, the two approximations $\underline{S}_n$ and $\overline{S}_n$ get closer and closer together. In fact, in the case in which f is continuous in $[a, b]$, it can be shown that $\lim_{n \to \infty} (\overline{S}_n - \underline{S}_n) = 0$; that is, $\lim_{n \to \infty} \overline{S}_n = \lim_{n \to \infty} \underline{S}_n$, and we define the area under the curve to be this common limit:

$$A = \lim_{n \to \infty} \overline{S}_n = \lim_{n \to \infty} \underline{S}_n.$$

If the function f is continuous in $[a, b]$, it is true that, even if we had not divided $[a, b]$ into *equal* subintervals and if we had picked an arbi-

---

† The notations $f(x_{i_m})$ and $f(x_{i_M})$ reflect the fact that a function continuous in a closed interval assumes a minimum and a maximum value for some values of the independent variable in the interval. This theorem is proved in more advanced courses in calculus.

trary value of the independent variable, say x_i, in the ith such subinterval with length Δx_i, then

$$\lim \underline{S}_n = \lim \overline{S}_n = \lim_{n \to \infty} \sum_{i=1}^{n} f(x_i)\, \Delta x_i = A$$

so long as the number of subintervals increases in such a way that the length of the longest subinterval goes to zero as n becomes large. Accordingly, the symbol usually used for the limit

$$\lim_{n \to \infty} \sum_{i=1}^{n} f(x_i)\, \Delta x_i \quad \text{is} \quad \int_{a}^{b} f(x)\, dx,$$

which is read, "the definite integral of f over $[a, b]$." It should be noted that, given f and the integral $[a, b]$, the definite integral is a certain real number which is a measure of the area under f in the interval $[a, b]$. The fact that the name of the independent variable has no bearing on this number leads some authors to adopt the notation $\int_{a}^{b} f$ for the definite integral. We shall use both notations in this text, since the traditional notation frequently has advantages over the more streamlined one. These advantages are: (1) it suggests the origin of the integral as the limit of a sum; (2) it obviates the need for inventing names for every function [we may simply use the value $f(x)$ of the function in this notation]; and (3) in expressions in which we have several variables, it allows us unambiguously to designate the independent variable for the function.

Unfortunately, the calculation of areas from this definition is usually quite cumbersome.

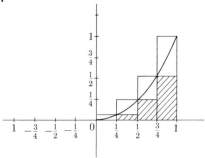

EXAMPLE 6–5.1. Find the area under the graph of

$$f = \{(x, x^2)\}$$

in the interval $[0, 1]$.

If we take n to be 4, $(b - a)/n = (1 - 0)/4 = \frac{1}{4}$, and since $f(x) = x^2$ is strictly increasing in $[0, 1]$, the minimum value, $f(x_{i_m})$, occurs at the left end point of the ith subinterval and is $[(i - 1)/4]^2$; similarly, the maximum occurs at the right end point of the interval, and $f(x_{i_M}) = (i/4)^2$.

$$\underline{S}_4 = \sum_{i=1}^{4} \left(\frac{i - 1}{4}\right)^2 \frac{1}{4} = \frac{1}{4^3} \sum_{i=1}^{4} (i - 1)^2$$

$$= \frac{1}{4^3} (0 + 1 + 4 + 9) = \frac{14}{64} = \frac{7}{32}.$$

$$\overline{S}_4 = \sum_{i=1}^{4} \left(\frac{i}{4}\right)^2 \cdot \frac{1}{4} = \frac{1}{4^3} \sum_{i=1}^{4} i^2$$

$$= \frac{1}{4^3} (1 + 4 + 9 + 16) = \frac{30}{64} = \frac{15}{32}.$$

$$\underline{S}_n = \sum_{i=1}^{n} \left(\frac{i - 1}{n}\right)^2 \cdot \frac{1}{n} = \frac{1}{n^3} \sum_{i=1}^{n} (i - 1)^2$$

$$= \frac{1}{n^3} \cdot \frac{(n - 1)(n)(2n - 1)}{6} .^{\dagger}$$

$$\overline{S}_n = \sum_{i=1}^{n} \left(\frac{i}{n}\right)^2 \cdot \frac{1}{n} = \frac{1}{n^3} \sum_{i=1}^{n} i^2 = \frac{1}{n^3} \cdot \frac{n(n + 1)(2n + 1)}{6} .^{\dagger}$$

Thus

$$\frac{(1 - 1/n)(1)(2 - 1/n)}{6} \le \int_0^1 f \le \frac{1(1 + 1/n)(2 + 1/n)}{6} ,$$

and

$$\int_0^1 f = \lim_{n \to \infty} \frac{(1 - 1/n)(2 - 1/n)}{6} = \lim_{n \to \infty} \frac{1(1 + 1/n)(2 + 1/n)}{6} = \frac{1}{3} .$$

In general, the calculation of areas from the definition of the definite integral is too difficult. Instead, we use the result known as the fundamental theorem of integral calculus.

---

† See Exercise 6 in Section 3–2.

Before considering this remarkable theorem, we look at a few properties of the definite integral. The definition was made under the assumption that f was positive and continuous in the interval $[a, b]$. For applications other than finding areas, it is useful to be able to extend the definition to include functions which may not be positive throughout $[a, b]$. In intervals in which $f(x) < 0$, we leave the definition unchanged; only the interpretation of the integral as an area need be modified. The terms $f(x_i)\,\Delta x_i$ of the sum will be negative if $f(x_i) < 0$, and the integral will be the negative of the area below the x-axis.

It is also useful to define $\int_a^b f$ when $a \not< b$.

Definition 6–5.1. $\displaystyle\int_a^a f = 0.$

Definition 6–5.2. $\displaystyle\int_a^b f = -\int_b^a f.$

Definition 6–5.1 simply formalizes the intuitive notion that the area under a curve over an interval of length zero should be zero; Definition 6–5.2 gives meaning to $\int_a^b f$ when $a > b$. This definition seems reasonable, since one might think of the Δx_i in $\int_a^b f$ as the negatives of the lengths of the subintervals for the segment of the x-axis from b to a, in which $b < a$.

In addition to these definitions which give meaning to $\int_a^b f$, regardless of the positions of a and b on the x-axis, some other properties of the definite integral are useful.

$$(1) \quad \int_a^b cf = c\int_a^b f, \qquad c \text{ a constant.}$$

$$(2) \quad \int_a^b (f + g) = \int_a^b f + \int_a^b g.$$

$$(3) \quad \int_a^b f + \int_b^c f = \int_a^c f.$$

Properties (1) and (2) follow from properties of limits (see Exercises 6 and 7 of Section 5–2), while (3) states the so-called additive property of integrals. Intuitively, the area under the curve f in the interval $[a, b]$, plus the area under the curve f in the interval $[b, c]$, should be the area under the curve in the interval $[a, c]$, since

$$[a, c] = [a, b] \cup [b, c].$$

EXERCISES

1. Compute:

   (a) $\sum_{i=1}^{5} i.$ (b) $\sum_{i=1}^{3} i^2.$ (c) $\sum_{i=1}^{4} i^3.$

2. Find the upper and lower approximations to the area of the circle with radius 1 if the number of sides of the inscribed and circumscribed regular polygons is 8.

3. (a) Find $\int_0^1 f$ if f is the constant function defined by $f(x) = 2$.
   (b) What is $\int_a^b c$, where c is a constant function?

4. For the identity function $I = \{(x, x)\}$, sketch the approximations $\underline{S}_4$ and $\overline{S}_4$ for the area under I in the interval $[0, 1]$. Find $\underline{S}_n$ and $\overline{S}_n$. Compute the area under the curve from the definition of the definite integral, and check your answer by computing the area in a different way.

5. Use properties (1) and (2) of the definite integral and the results of Example 6–5.1 and Exercise 3 to find $\int_0^1 g$ if $g(x) = 3x^2 - 2x$.

6. Suppose that $f(x) \geq 0$ in $[a, b]$ and $f(x) < 0$ in $]b, c]$. What would be the geometric interpretation of $\int_a^c |f|$?

7. Use the results of this section to find

   (a) $\int_0^1 2x \, dx.$ (b) $\int_0^1 (ax + b) \, dx.$

   (c) $\int_0^1 (x - 2x^2) \, dx.$ (d) $\int_0^1 (ax^2 + bx + c) \, dx.$

6–6 THE FUNDAMENTAL THEOREM OF INTEGRAL CALCULUS

One of the more foolish controversies in the history of mathematics is the nationalistic squabble over the credit for the invention of the calculus. The two great ideas, the limits involved in the solution of the problems of finding tangents to curves and areas under curves, were undoubtedly fairly well known at the middle of the seventeenth century. Both Descartes and Fermat had methods for finding tangents to curves, while Archimedes, in the third century B.C., had solved many of the problems of determining areas and volumes. The distinctive additional ingredient, aside from changes of notation and a systematic formulation of the results, was the fundamental theorem of integral calculus. This connecting link between the differential and the integral calculus was the independent contribution of Newton and Leibniz.

The theorem states that a function F which has the function f as its derivative throughout the interval $[a, b]$ serves to evaluate the definite integral: $\int_a^b f = F(b) - F(a)$.

Theorem 6–6.1

> *If F is any function with the property that $F' = f$ in $[a, b]$, then $\int_a^b f = F(b) - F(a)$.*

We do not pretend to give a formal proof of the fundamental theorem but content ourselves with an outline of the principal ideas in the proof.

We first define $G(x) = \int_a^x f$. The crux of the proof then lies in showing that $G'(x) = f(x)$. This, of course, involves the definition of $G'(x)$ and the properties of the definite integral. Next, if F and G are any two functions such that $F' = G'$, $F = G + C$, where C is a constant. Then

$$F(x) = G(x) + C$$

and

$$F(a) = G(a) + C.$$

Since $G(a) = \int_a^a f = 0$,

$$F(a) = C,$$

or

$$G(x) = F(x) - F(a),$$

and

$$G(b) = F(b) - F(a).$$

Therefore,

$$\int_a^b f = F(b) - F(a), \qquad \text{since} \qquad G(x) = \int_a^x f.$$

This theorem enables us to calculate the value of any definite integral, $\int_a^b f$, provided we can find a function F such that $F' = f$. Such a function F is called an *antiderivative* of f. The second result used in the proof of the fundamental theorem states that any two antiderivatives of a function differ by a constant.

Besides the obvious advantage of avoiding the tedious and difficult process of finding areas from the definition of the definite integral, this new result furnishes the unifying link between the two branches of the calculus. There are numerous other applications of the integral calculus, some of which we shall consider in the next section.

EXERCISES

1. Let f be a function continuous in $[a, b]$, and let the area under the graph of f in $[a, b]$ be A. Argue that there is a value of x in $[a, b]$, say $\bar{x}$, such that $A = f(\bar{x})(b - a)$.

2. For $f = \{(x, x^2)\}$ in the interval $[0, 1]$, find the $\bar{x}$ of Exercise 1.

3. If $G(x) = \int_a^z f$, find

$$\frac{G(x + h) - G(x)}{h}.$$

4. Use the results of Exercises 1 and 3 to show that $G'(x) = f(x)$. [*Hint:* $[G(x + h) - G(x)]/h = f(\bar{x})$.]

5. Find an antiderivative for each of the following functions. [*Hint:* See the Exercises in Section 6–2.]

(a) $f = \{(x, 0)\}$.   (b) $f = \{(x, 1)\}$.
(c) $f = \{(x, c)\}$.   (d) $f = \{(x, x)\}$.
(e) $f = \{(x, x^2)\}$.   (f) $f = \{(x, 2x)\}$.
(g) $f = \{(x, 2x^2)\}$.   (h) $f = \{(x, x^3)\}$.
(i) $f = \{(x, x^n)\}$.

6–7 APPLICATIONS OF THE DEFINITE INTEGRAL

In developing the limit which we called the derivative to solve the problem of determining the tangent to a curve at a point, we found that the resulting limit had wider application. In fact, the concept of the rate of change of one varying quantity with respect to another is probably more useful than the solution to the original tangent problem. This concept, in turn, has been used to solve maximum and minimum problems in literally hundreds of different applications. The derivative was also useful in determining the slope of a curve and in finding critical points needed in sketching it.

In much the same way, the new limit which we have been concerned with in the last few sections turns out to have many applications more important than simply finding areas under curves. This limit, the definite integral, has been applied in almost every area of scientific investigation—not only in the natural sciences but in the social sciences as well. Most of these applications are, on the face of them, far removed from our original problem of determining the area under a curve.

We now give a few illustrations to show the power of this idea.

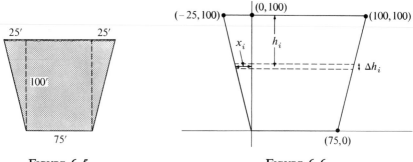

FIGURE 6–5

FIGURE 6–6

EXAMPLE 6–7.1. Find the force which the face of the dam pictured in Fig. 6–5 must withstand.

Solution. A horizontal surface submerged in water is subjected to a downward force equal to the weight of the column of water directly above it. Since water exerts equal pressure in all directions, if we take a sufficiently thin strip, the pressure on this strip will be approximately the same as if it were horizontal rather than vertical. The pressure would then be the product of the volume of the column of water above the strip and the weight of a cubic foot of water w. The volume of the column of water, in turn, is the product of the area of the strip times the depth of the strip below the surface of the water. (See Fig. 6–6.)

The force on the entire face of the dam is approximately equal to the sum of the forces on the small strips. The force on the thin strip h_i feet below the surface, with area ΔA_i, is $wh_i \, \Delta A_i$. Thus if we break up the height of 100 feet into thin strips of width Δh_i, an approximation to the force on the face of the dam is $\sum_{i=1}^{n} wh_i \, \Delta A_i$. Let $\Delta A_i = l_i \, \Delta h_i$, where l_i is the length of the ith strip. Hence F, the force on the face of the dam, is approximately $\sum_{i=1}^{n} wh_i l_i \, \Delta h_i$. But by similar triangles,

$$\frac{x_i}{100 - h_i} = \frac{25}{100} \quad \text{and} \quad x_i = \tfrac{1}{4}(100 - h_i).$$

Since $l_i = 2x_i + 75$, we may replace l_i by $\tfrac{1}{2}(100 - h_i) + 75$. Hence F is approximately

$$\sum_{i=1}^{n} wh_i(\tfrac{1}{2}(100 - h_i) + 75) \, \Delta h_i.$$

If we now make the number of strips larger and larger in such a way that the width Δh_i gets smaller and smaller, taking the limit as $n \to \infty$, we have

$$F = \int_0^{100} wh(\tfrac{1}{2}(100 - h) + 75)\, dh,$$

or, if $f(h) = h(\tfrac{1}{2}(100 - h) + 75)$,

$$F = \int_0^{100} w f(h)\, dh.$$

But this is simply a definite integral which we can compute by using the techniques of the previous section.

EXAMPLE 6–7.2. Find the length of the arc of the curved line $y = f(x)$ joining $(a, f(a))$ and $(b, f(b))$.

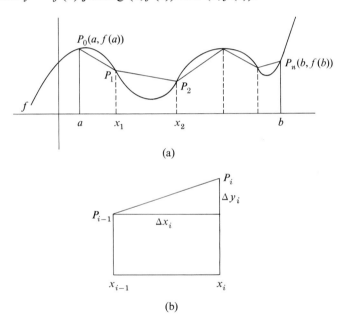

(a)

(b)

Solution. We could approximate the length by taking $n - 1$ intermediate points $(P_i, i = 1, 2, \ldots, n - 1)$ on the arc and joining them with straight line segments. The length of the broken line thus formed would approximate the length of the arc. The length of the ith straight-line segment would be $\sqrt{\Delta x_i^2 + \Delta y_i^2}$, and an approximation to the length of the arc would be

$$\sum_{i=1}^n \sqrt{\Delta x_i^2 + \Delta y_i^2} = \sum_{i=1}^n \sqrt{1 + (\Delta y_i^2/\Delta x_i^2)}\, \Delta x_i.$$

Hence it would be reasonable to suppose that the length of the arc is

$$L = \lim_{n \to \infty} \sum_{i=1}^{n} \sqrt{1 + (\Delta y_i/\Delta x_i)^2} \, \Delta x_i,$$

where $\Delta x_i \to 0$ as $n \to \infty$. But this is just equal to $\int_a^b \sqrt{1 + (f'(x))^2} \, dx$, $(\lim_{\Delta x \to 0} (\Delta y/\Delta x) = f'(x))$.†

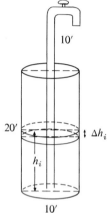

EXAMPLE 6-7.3. Find the work done in pumping the water contained in a cylindrical tank 10 feet in diameter and 20 feet deep to a faucet 10 feet above the tank.

Solution. The work done is the product of the force needed to move the water and the distance through which it is moved. As in the previous problem, we consider that all of a layer of water must be moved through approximately the same distance.

Then to move the layer of water of thickness Δh_i, we need a force equal to the weight of a cubic foot of water w times the volume of water $\pi 5^2 \, \Delta h_i$. This layer of water must be moved through a distance of $(30 - h_i)$ feet. Therefore, the work done in moving this layer to the faucet is

$$(30 - h_i)w\pi 5^2 \, \Delta h_i.$$

If we imagine the tank full of water sliced into n thin layers and move each layer in succession from the top, the work done in emptying the tank is approximately

$$\sum_{i=1}^{n} (30 - h_i)w\pi 5^2 \, \Delta h_i \quad \text{or} \quad 25w\pi \sum_{i=1}^{n} (30 - h_i) \, \Delta h_i.$$

If we take the limit as the number of layers is increased by making them thinner and thinner, we get

$$\text{Work} = 25w\pi \int_0^{20} (30 - h) \, dh.$$

But this is simply a definite integral, as before.

---

† The justification for this result requires several sophisticated theorems and is considerably more difficult than we have indicated.

EXAMPLE 6–7.4. Find the volume of the solid obtained by revolving the area under the curve given by $f(x) = x^2$ in the interval $[0, 1]$ about the x-axis.

Solution.   Divide the interval $[0, 1]$ into n subintervals Δx_i, $i = 1, 2, \ldots, n$. Approximate the volume obtained in the ith subinterval by a right circular cylinder of radius $f(x_i)$ and thickness Δx_i. The volume of this ith slice is approximately $\pi r^2 h = \pi (f(x_i))^2 \Delta x_i$. An approximation to the total volume is

$$\sum_{i=1}^{n} \pi (f(x_i))^2 \Delta x_i.$$

Taking the limit as $n \to \infty$ in such a way that $\Delta x_i \to 0$, we have

$$\text{Volume} = \int_0^1 \pi (f(x))^2 \, dx = \pi \int_0^1 x^4 \, dx.$$

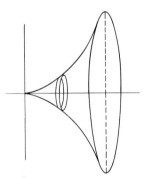

Since $F'(x) = x^4$ for $F(x) = x^5/5$,

$$\text{Volume} = \pi(\tfrac{1}{5} - 0) = \frac{\pi}{5} \text{ cubic units.}$$

These examples are only a few of the typical applications which have been found for the definite integral. Undoubtedly, it is one of the most useful ideas to be found in all mathematics.

EXERCISES

1. Find the force on the end of a triangular trough 10 feet long if it is full of water and a cross section is an equilateral triangle of altitude 6 inches.

2. Set up the integral for finding the length of the arc of the parabola $x^2 + 2x + 3$ in the interval $[0, 1]$.

3. If $w = 62.5$ pounds, find the work done in the problem of Example 6–7.3.

4. Find the volume of the cone obtained by revolving the area under $f = \{(x, x^2)\}$ in the interval $[0, 2]$ about the x-axis.

5. Find the volume obtained by revolving the area bounded by $f = \{(x, x^2)\}$, the vertical line through $(1, 0)$, and the x-axis, about the y-axis.

6–8 SUMMARY

In Chapters 5 and 6, we dealt with one of the most brilliant achievements in all of mathematics, the systematic employment of the limit concept. This idea, together with the idea of a function, makes possible the vast body of knowledge called mathematical analysis. The calculus is the basic tool in this part of mathematics. While we have only scratched the surface of this subject, we have investigated the two fundamental limits which lie at the heart of the calculus, the derivative and the definite integral. These limits are basic to the formulation of many of the most important concepts in modern science.

REVIEW EXERCISES

1. Define:
    (a) Derivative.
    (b) Antiderivative.
    (c) Tangent to the curve $y = f(x)$ at $x = a$.
    (d) Area under the curve $y = f(x)$ in the interval $[a, b]$.
    (e) Instantaneous speed.

2. State and explain the significance of the Fundamental Theorem of Integral Calculus.

3. Find the derivative of each of the following by finding

$$\lim_{h \to 0} \frac{f(x + h) - f(x)}{h} :$$

    (a) $f(x) = x + 2$. (b) $f(x) = x^2 + 1$. (c) $f(x) = mx + b$.

4. Find the function whose graph is the tangent to the curve:
    (a) $y = 2x$, where $x = 2$.
    (b) $y = 3x^2$, where $x = 1$.
    *(c) $y = 1/x$, where $x = 2$.

5. For what values of x is the tangent to the curve $y = x^2 - 4x + 5$ horizontal?

6. Find the relative maxima and minima, and sketch the graph of the curve:
    (a) $y = \frac{1}{3}x^3 - \frac{1}{2}x^2 - 6x + 2$.
    (b) $y = x^3 - 6x^2 + 12x - 8$.

7. A projectile is thrown straight up from the ground with an initial velocity of 96 feet per second. Its height after t seconds is given by $h = 96t - 16t^2$, where h is measured in feet. After how many seconds does the projectile reach its maximum height? What is the maximum height?

8. If 400 people will attend a moving picture theater when the admission price is 30 cents, and if the attendance decreases by 40 for each 10 cents added to the price, then what admission price will yield the greatest gross receipts?

9. Find the equation of the curve whose tangent has the slope 3 at all values of x and passes through the point $(2, 7)$.

10. Find the equation of the curve whose tangent has the slope $2x - 3$ at all values of x and passes through the point $(1, 3)$.

11. Find the area under the curve $y = 3x + 4$ from $x = 1$ to $x = 4$.

12. Find the area under the curve $y = \frac{1}{2}x^2$ from $x = 1$ to $x = 4$.

13. Find the area under the curve $y = x^2 - x + 15$ from $x = 2$ to $x = 5$.

14. (a) Find the relative maxima and minima, the interval in which the curve is concave upward, and sketch the graph of $f(x) = x^3 - 3x$.
    (b) Find the area under this curve in the interval $[-\sqrt{3}, 0]$.

15. Find the relative maxima and minima, and sketch the graph of the function defined by $f(x) = 2x^3 - 3x^2 - 12x$. Find the integral of $f(x)$ in the interval $[-2, -1]$, and interpret geometrically.

$+$16. Prove that $D(f \cdot g) = f \cdot Dg + g \cdot Df$.

$*+$17. Use the results of Exercise 16 and mathematical induction to prove that if $f(x) = x^n, f'(x) = nx^{n-1}$ for any positive integer n.

Suggested Readings

ALLENDOERFER and OAKLEY, *Principles of Mathematics*, second edition, McGraw-Hill, New York, 1963, Chs. 10 and 11, pp. 354–401.

*COOLIDGE, J. L., "The Story of Tangents," from the *American Mathematical Monthly*, Vol. 58 (1951), pp. 449–462.

*NEWMAN, J. R., "Newton," in *The World of Mathematics*, Simon and Schuster, New York, 1956, Vol. I, pp. 254–285; "The Analyst," by Bishop Berkeley, Vol. I, pp. 286–293.

RICHARDSON, M., *Fundamentals of Mathematics*, Macmillan, New York, 1958, Ch. 11, pp. 309–341.

*ROSENTHAL, R. A., "The History of the Calculus," from the *American Mathematical Monthly*, Vol. 58 (1951), pp. 75–86.

*TITCHMARSH, E. C., *Mathematics for the General Reader*, Doubleday Anchor Books, Garden City, N. Y., 1959, Chs. 13, 14, pp. 152–191.

General References

BELL, E. T., *Men of Mathematics*, Simon and Schuster, New York, 1937, Chs. 6 and 7.

BOYER, C. B., *The History of the Calculus*, Dover, New York, 1949.

COURANT and ROBBINS, *What Is Mathematics?*, Oxford University Press, New York, 1941.

EVES, H., *An Introduction to the History of Mathematics*, Rinehart, New York, 1956, Ch. 11, pp. 314–347.

HOOPER, A., *Makers of Mathematics*, Random House, New York, 1948.

LIEBER, L. R. and H. G., *Infinity*, Rinehart, New York, 1953.

MAY, K. O., *Elements of Mathematics*, Addison-Wesley, Reading, Mass., 1959, Ch. 7.

7 | COUNTING AND PROBABILITY

7–1 PERMUTATIONS AND COMBINATIONS

In Chapter 3 we considered Peano's axioms for the natural numbers, which we referred to from time to time as "counting numbers." Counting is very important in another area of mathematics, the theory of probability. We shall consider briefly in the latter part of this chapter the mathematical theory of probability. However, since some of the fundamental ideas in this theory merely involve systematic ways of counting, we shall first consider a few of the special methods of counting.

Suppose that a guest in your house brings five Danish candlesticks, one green, one blue, one yellow, one red, and one purple, back from a visit to Denmark. He tells you that you may choose any two you would like. How many choices do you have? Suppose that we try to list the choices. We represent the set of candlesticks by $S = \{G, B, Y, R, P\}$. Our problem is to list all the different subsets containing two members: $\{G, B\}$, $\{G, Y\}$, $\{G, R\}$, $\{G, P\}$, $\{B, Y\}$, $\{B, R\}$, $\{B, P\}$, $\{Y, R\}$, $\{Y, P\}$, $\{R, P\}$.

We say that each choice is a *combination* of five things taken two at a time; the number of such combinations is denoted by the symbols $\binom{5}{2} = C_2^5 = 10$. Suppose that we then wanted to set the candlesticks on the mantel. We could arrange each of the combinations in two ways; for example, green on the left and blue on the right, or blue on the left and green on the right. The number of ways to arrange the pairs of candlesticks would then be twice the number of combinations, $2 \cdot 10 = 20$. Another way to look at the number of arrangements would be to say that we could choose the candlestick to be placed on the left in any one of five ways, and after making this choice, we could select the one to go on the right from the remaining candlesticks in any of four ways. Thus the number of possible ways to arrange the pairs of candlesticks would be $5 \cdot 4 = 20$. When the order in which we arrange the set is taken into account, we call this arrangement a *permutation*, and use the notation $P_2^5 = 5 \cdot 4$ for the number of possible permutations or arrangements of the five objects taken two at a time.

If, instead of arranging two objects selected from a set of five, we consider the problem of counting the number of different ways to arrange, say, r objects selected from a set of n objects, we can use the same idea. We choose the first object to go on the extreme left in any one of n ways; after this choice has been made, we choose the one to go next to it from the remaining $n - 1$ objects in any one of $n - 1$ ways, and so on. The number of different ways of arranging in a row r objects taken from a set of n objects would then be

$$P_r^n = \underbrace{n(n - 1)(n - 2) \cdots [n - (r - 1)]}_{r \text{ factors}} \cdot$$

If we use the factorial notation introduced in the Exercises in Section 3–2,

$$P_r^n = \frac{n(n - 1)(n - 2) \cdots (n - r + 1)(n - r) \cdots 1}{(n - r) \cdots 1},$$

or

$$(1) \qquad \boxed{P_r^n = \frac{n!}{(n - r)!} \cdot}$$

If we choose to count the number of arrangements of all n things taken n at a time, we should get

$$P_n^n = n(n - 1)(n - 2) \cdots 1 = n!.$$

Since in the formula $n!/(n - r)!$ this would become $n!/0!$, it is convenient both here and in other connections to define $0!$ to be 1. With this understanding, the formula (1) holds for all r greater than or equal to zero and less than or equal to n.

We now consider generalizing our original problem to that of finding the number of ways to select r objects from a set of n objects (when we do not care about the order in which the objects are selected or arranged). A formula for C_r^n is obtained by noting that for each one of the C_r^n subsets of r objects selected, we could arrange each subset in $r!$ ways. Hence

$$P_r^n = r! C_r^n,$$

or

$$C_r^n = \frac{P_r^n}{r!} = \frac{n!}{r!(n-r)!}$$

and we have the formula

(2)
$$\binom{n}{r} = C_r^n = \frac{n!}{r!(n-r)!}$$

for the number of ways of selecting r objects from a given set of n objects.

Formula (2) gives us

$$\binom{5}{2} = \frac{5!}{2!(5-2)!} = \frac{5!}{2!3!} = \frac{5 \cdot 4}{2 \cdot 1} = 10$$

for the candlestick problem which we considered originally.

EXERCISES

1. Calculate $\binom{5}{3}$, $\binom{3}{2}$, $\binom{5}{0}$, P_5^{10}, P_5^5, C_2^4.

+2. Show that $C_r^n = C_{n-r}^n$.

3. In how many ways can we select
   (a) a committee of 5 members from a class of 25 members?
   (b) a jury of 12 from a panel of 30 eligible persons?
   (c) 3 courses from a course list containing 45 courses?
   (d) a poker hand of 5 cards from a deck of 52 cards?
   (e) a bridge hand of 13 cards from a deck of 52 cards?

4. In how many ways can we
   (a) arrange 20 books on a shelf?
   (b) arrange 7 people in a row for a group picture?
   (c) organize a baseball team from a squad of 15?
   (d) form 5-digit numbers?
   (e) form new 7-digit telephone numbers?

5. Given five different signal flags, how many signals can be made by arranging them on a vertical mast, if at least two flags must be used for each signal?

6. Twelve boys make up a basketball squad. Five can play forward, two center, and five guard. In how many ways can the coach make up the team?

7. Ten points are selected on the circumference of a circle. How many chords can be drawn by joining them in all possible ways? How many triangles can be formed, using the points as vertices?

8. There are eight chairs in a row. In how many ways can two people be seated in the row? In how many of these ways will the two people be sitting next to each other?

*9. How many different 4-digit numbers can be formed from the digits 1, 1, 2, 2, 3, 3.

10. In how many ways can ten books be arranged on a shelf if one set of three volumes is kept together in the order Vol. I, Vol. II, Vol. III?

11. Show that $C_4^7 + C_3^7 = C_4^8$.

+12. Prove that $\binom{n}{r-1} + \binom{n}{r} = \binom{n+1}{r}$, $1 \leq r \leq n$.

7–2 THE BINOMIAL THEOREM

In developing the formula for the number of permutations of n objects taken r at a time in the last section, we made use of a rather fundamental principle of counting, namely, *if one member of a given set can be selected in n ways and after that member has been selected, a second member can be selected in m ways, the two selections can be made in the given order in n · m ways.*

Suppose that we look again at the problem of determining the number of subsets of a set with n elements (Exercise 3 in the Exercises in Section 1–2). Let $S = \{a_1, a_2, \ldots, a_n\}$. We form subsets X of S in the following way. We look at each element of S in turn, beginning with a_1, and notice that we have two choices, either $a_1 \in X$ or $a_1 \notin X$; that is, so far as a_1 is concerned, there are two possibilities in forming X. Similarly, either $a_2 \in X$ or $a_2 \notin X$. Hence if we consider only the two elements a_1 and a_2, we have $2 \cdot 2$ ways of forming subsets. The subsets are $\emptyset$ (select neither one), $\{a_1\}$ (select a_1 but not a_2), $\{a_2\}$ (select a_2 but not a_1), $\{a_1, a_2\}$ (select both). If we now consider a_3, for each of the previous choices we may either add a_3 to the subset previously formed or not add it. We thus have $2 \cdot 2 \cdot 2$ subsets involving only a_1, a_2, a_3. If we continue in this way, we have

$$\underbrace{2 \cdot 2 \cdots 2}_{n \text{ factors}} = 2^n$$

ways of forming subsets from a set containing n objects.

However, we could look at this another way. We could form the subsets by considering how many different subsets we might form containing a particular number of elements, say r elements. There would be the subset containing no elements, $\emptyset$. In a previous exercise we have shown that there is only one such set. This number of subsets containing no elements could be thought of as the number of ways of selecting zero elements from among n elements; that is, $C_0^n = 1$. Then we would like to find out how many subsets there are consisting of just one element. The answer is clearly $C_1^n = n$. In the same way, there are C_2^n subsets containing exactly 2 elements, etc. In fact, the total number of subsets which we could form is given by

$$C_0^n + C_1^n + C_2^n + \cdots + C_n^n.$$

By our previous count, we have seen that this sum is just 2^n. We have then the result that $2^n = C_0^n + C_1^n + C_2^n + \cdots + C_n^n$.

To save space, we use the sigma notation introduced in Section 6–5. We write $\sum_{i=0}^{n} C_i^n$ for $C_0^n + C_1^n + C_2^n + \cdots + C_n^n$. Then

$$\sum_{i=0}^{n} C_i^n = 2^n = (1 + 1)^n.$$

The mathematician's special prerogative is to generalize; now suppose that we wished to multiply n factors $(1 + x)$ together.

$$\underbrace{(1 + x)(1 + x) \cdots (1 + x)}_{n \text{ factors}} = (1 + x)^n.$$

All the terms in the product are obtained by multiplying together either a 1 or an x from each of the n factors. For example, if we select a one from each of the factors, the term which appears in the product will be

$$\underbrace{1 \cdot 1 \cdots 1}_{n \text{ factors}} = 1.$$

If we select one x and $n - 1$ ones, the term in the product will be

$$\underbrace{x \cdot 1 \cdot 1 \ldots 1}_{n-1 \text{ factors}}.$$

But we can select the x from any one of the n factors; hence there will be C_1^n terms x in the product. Similarly, there will be C_2^n terms

$$x^2 \cdot \underbrace{1 \cdot 1 \cdots 1}_{n-2 \text{ factors}};$$

etc. In fact, the product can be written

$$(1 + x)^n = C_0^n(1) + C_1^n x + C_2^n x^2 + \cdots + C_n^n x^n$$

or

$$(1 + x)^n = \sum_{i=0}^{n} C_i^n x^i.$$

This again is a special case of a slightly more general result. Suppose that we consider the product

$$(a + b)^n = \underbrace{(a + b)(a + b) \cdots (a + b)}_{n \text{ factors}}.$$

Then the terms in the product will take the form $a^{n-i}b^i$, and since b was selected from each of i factors, the choice from the remaining $n - i$ factors would have to be a.

Consequently, there will be C_i^n terms of the form $a^{n-i}b^i$, and the product is

$$(a + b)^n = \sum_{i=0}^{n} C_i^n a^{n-i} b^i = \sum_{i=0}^{n} \binom{n}{i} a^{n-i} b^i.$$

This last result is called the *binomial theorem*, and the number $\binom{n}{i}$ is called a *binomial coefficient*, since it counts the number of times the term $a^{n-i}b^i$ appears in the product of the n "binomial factors" $(a + b)$.

Theorem 7–2.1. *The Binomial Theorem*

If n is any natural number,

$$(a + b)^n = \sum_{i=0}^{n} \binom{n}{i} a^{n-i} b^i.$$

EXERCISES

1. Compute:

(a) $\displaystyle\sum_{i=0}^{4} \binom{4}{i}.$

(b) $\displaystyle\sum_{i=0}^{3} \binom{3}{i} a^{3-i} b^i.$

2. Expand the following, using the binomial theorem.

    (a) $(1 + 2)^4$.   (b) $(1 + x)^3$.   (c) $(x + y)^5$.

    (d) $(2 + 3x)^7$.   (e) $(a - b)^6$.   (f) $[2a - (b/a)]^3$.

3. What is the coefficient of x^{14} in the product $(1 + x)^{27}$?

4. What is the coefficient of x^5 in $(1 + x^2)^{12}$?

5. The following array is called Pascal's Triangle.

$$
\begin{array}{ccccccccc}
 & & & & 1 & & & & \\
 & & & 1 & & 1 & & & \\
 & & 1 & & 2 & & 1 & & \\
 & 1 & & 3 & & 3 & & 1 & \\
1 & & 4 & & 6 & & 4 & & 1 \\
 & & & & \vdots & & & &
\end{array}
$$

How is it constructed? Extend it to 10 rows. What does it have to do with the binomial theorem?

6. Use the binomial theorem to find an approximation to three decimal places of:

    (a) $(1.002)^5$. [*Hint:* Write 1.002 as $(1 + 0.002)$.]

    (b) $(0.998)^{10}$.

    (c) $(1.04)^4$.

7. Use the binomial theorem to expand $(1 + x + y)^4$.

*8. Show that $\sum_{r=0}^{n} (-1)^r C_r^n = 0$.

7–3 PROBABILITY

Both the statements, "It will probably rain tomorrow," and "The probability of getting a bridge hand containing 13 spades is 13!39!/52!," have something to say about uncertain events. When the Weather Bureau's prediction is that it will rain tomorrow, studies have shown that such predictions are correct about 80 percent of the time. Still, from experience, we know that despite this record, tomorrow's weather is rather uncertain.

The mathematical theory used to analyze and formulate statements about uncertain events is called the theory of probability. There are many views on just what "probability" means, but there is rather general agreement in the case of uncertain events which have only a finite number of possible outcomes. It is this kind of probability which we wish to examine and formulate as a mathematical theory.

The terminology of sets is again the most useful tool in stating this theory. We consider the universe of discourse U as the set of all conceivable outcomes of a given experiment. We call this set U a *sample space*. Any subset of U is called an *event*. We wish to consider a function $P = \{(X, P(X))\}$ in $U \times R$ (where U is the universe of discourse and R is the set of real numbers) which satisfies the following axioms:

> $\mathbf{A}_1$. $P(X) \geq 0$.
> $\mathbf{A}_2$. $P(U) = 1$.
> $\mathbf{A}_3$. If $A \cap B = \emptyset$, then $P(A \cup B) = P(A) + P(B)$.

Theorem 7–3.1

> $P(\overline{A}) = 1 - P(A)$.
>
> *Proof*
>
> | | |
> |---|---|
> | 1. $A \cap \overline{A} = \emptyset$. | Definition of $\overline{A}$ |
> | 2. $A \cup \overline{A} = U$. | Definition of $\overline{A}$ |
> | 3. $P(A \cup \overline{A}) = P(A) + P(\overline{A})$. | Step 1 and $\mathbf{A}_3$ |
> | 4. $P(U) = P(A) + P(\overline{A})$. | Step 2 |
> | 5. $1 = P(A) + P(\overline{A})$. | $\mathbf{A}_2$ |
> | 6. $P(\overline{A}) = 1 - P(A)$. | Properties of subtraction |

Theorem 7–3.2

> $P(\emptyset) = 0$.
>
> *Proof*
>
> | | |
> |---|---|
> | 1. $\emptyset = \overline{U}$. | Definition of null and universal sets |
> | 2. $P(\emptyset) = 1 - P(U)$. | Theorem 7–3.1 with $A = U$ and step 1 |
> | 3. $P(\emptyset) = 1 - 1$. | $\mathbf{A}_2$ |
> | 4. $P(\emptyset) = 0$. | |

Axiom $\mathbf{A}_3$ gives the probability of $A \cup B$ only if A and B are disjoint sets. The following theorem generalizes this result.

Theorem 7–3.3

> For all $A, B \in U, P(A \cup B) = P(A) + P(B) - P(A \cap B)$.
>
> *Proof*
>
> | | |
> |---|---|
> | 1. $A \cup B = (A \cap \overline{B}) \cup B$. | See Exercise 7, Section 1–3 |
> | 2. $(A \cap \overline{B}) \cap B = \emptyset$. | See Exercise 7, Section 1–3 |

3. $P(A \cup B) = P((A \cap \bar{B}) \cup B)$.   Step 1
4. $P(A \cup B) = P(A \cap \bar{B}) + P(B)$.   Steps 2, 3, and A_3
5. $A = (A \cap B) \cup (A \cap \bar{B})$.   See Exercise 7, Section 1–3
6. $(A \cap B) \cap (A \cap \bar{B}) = \emptyset$.   Why?
7. $P(A) = P[(A \cap B) \cup (A \cap \bar{B})]$.   Step 5
8. $P(A) = P(A \cap B) + P(A \cap \bar{B})$.   Steps 6, 7, and A_3
9. $P(A \cap \bar{B}) = P(A) - P(A \cap B)$.   Step 8
10. $P(A \cup B) = P(A) + P(B)$
               $- P(A \cap B)$.   Steps 4 and 8

If we examine the axioms and theorems which we have just established, we may make the following interpretations: For some experiment, the set of all possible outcomes is the set U. Any particular outcome is called an event. Axiom A_1 states that the probability associated with any event X by the probability function P is always a nonnegative real number. The event U itself is certain, since it represents every possible outcome; A_2 simply associates the real number 1 with this event. In Exercise 2 you are asked to show that for any $X \in U$, $0 \le P(X) \le 1$. Theorem 7–3.2 states that the probability of an impossible event is zero.

EXAMPLE 7–3.1. Suppose that we wish to determine the probability of a seven coming up in one roll of two dice.

Solution. We could construct a sample space consisting of every possible outcome of the roll of two dice. The set of possible outcomes would be $\{2, 3, 4, 5, 6, 7, 8, 9, 10, 11, 12\}$. If we wished to determine the probability of one of these eleven numbers coming up, we would be considering $P(U)$, the probability of a sure thing: $P(U) = 1$. If, on the other hand, we wish to find the probability of a 13 coming up, this is an impossible event and its probability would be $P(\emptyset) = 0$. However, our interest is in 7 coming up. The axioms do not tell us exactly how we are to assign values to the probability function, and we might think that a reasonable way would be to consider all of the 11 possible outcomes as equally likely and assign each the value $\frac{1}{11}$. Some experimenting, or even a little reflection, might lead you to doubt the validity of this assignment. Is it really probable that 2 comes up as often as 7? We know that 2 can occur only if both dice come up 1; while 7 may occur as $1 + 6$, $2 + 5$, $3 + 4$, $4 + 3$, $5 + 2$, and

6 + 1. It would seem that 7 should occur about 6 times as often as 2. Accordingly, a more reasonable way to assign values to the probability function in this experiment would be to consider the $6 \times 6 = 36$ possible combinations of faces which might occur in a roll of two dice and count the number of times each of the possible results 2, 3, 4, 5, 6, 7, 8, 9, 10, 11, 12 occurs. The following table lists all possible outcomes.

	1	2	3	4	5	6
1	(1, 1)	(1, 2)	(1, 3)	(1, 4)	(1, 5)	(1, 6)
2	(2, 1)	(2, 2)	(2, 3)	(2, 4)	(2, 5)	(2, 6)
3	(3, 1)	(3, 2)	(3, 3)	(3, 4)	(3, 5)	(3, 6)
4	(4, 1)	(4, 2)	(4, 3)	(4, 4)	(4, 5)	(4, 6)
5	(5, 1)	(5, 2)	(5, 3)	(5, 4)	(5, 5)	(5, 6)
6	(6, 1)	(6, 2)	(6, 3)	(6, 4)	(6, 5)	(6, 6)

We are actually interested in the sum of the faces of each of these outcomes.

	1	2	3	4	5	6
1	2	3	4	5	6	7
2	3	4	5	6	7	8
3	4	5	6	7	8	9
4	5	6	7	8	9	10
5	6	7	8	9	10	11
6	7	8	9	10	11	12

To assign the probabilities in a reasonable way, we tabulate the number of occurrences (frequency) of each of the eleven possible outcomes X and define $P(X)$ as frequency/36.

X(outcome)	2	3	4	5	6	7	8	9	10	11	12	None of these
f(frequency)	1	2	3	4	5	6	5	4	3	2	1	0
$P(X)$	$\frac{1}{36}$	$\frac{1}{18}$	$\frac{1}{12}$	$\frac{1}{9}$	$\frac{5}{36}$	$\frac{1}{6}$	$\frac{5}{36}$	$\frac{1}{9}$	$\frac{1}{12}$	$\frac{1}{18}$	$\frac{1}{36}$	0

It is easy to check that this definition of the probability function P satisfies axioms A_1 through A_3.

Of course, if one or both of the dice were loaded, this assignment of probabilities would not be realistic. It might be that 11 would be much more likely than 7. (How could this happen?)

The axioms which we have stated do not determine either the sample space or the assignment of probabilities; they simply give us a framework in which to analyze experiments.

If each of the possible outcomes in a finite sample space is equally likely, a reasonable way to assign values to the probability function associated with the experiment is

$$P(X) = \frac{\text{frequency of } X \text{ in the sample space}}{\text{total number of elements in the sample space}}.$$

The results of Sections 7–1 and 7–2 on permutations and combinations and the binomial theorem are often useful in assigning values to probability functions.

> EXAMPLE 7–3.2. Find the probability of getting a bridge hand containing 13 spades.

> *Solution.* The number of possible bridge hands is C_{13}^{52}, while the number of hands containing 13 spades is $C_{13}^{13} = 1$. Hence the probability of obtaining a hand containing 13 spades is

$$\frac{1}{C_{13}^{52}} = \frac{1}{52!/13!39!} = \frac{13!39!}{52!}.$$

(This assumes, of course, that all hands are equally likely.)

EXERCISES

1. Show that for any $A \in U$, $P(A) \leq 1$, and hence that the range of $P \subset [0, 1]$.

2. Prove that $P(A \cup B) \leq P(A) + P(B)$.

3. What is the probability that either 7 or 11 comes up in one roll of two dice?

4. What is the probability that an even number comes up? an odd number?

5. If one is drawing a single card from a deck of 52 cards, find the probability that a heart or a face card (jack, queen, king, or ace) will be drawn.

6. How many different car tags may be made if each tag consists of two letters and five numbers? What is the probability of getting your phone number on your license plate?

7. What is the probability that in a room containing thirteen people two of them will have birthdays in the same month?

*8. What is the probability that in a room containing k people, no two of them have the same birthday? that at least two have the same birthday? Find the approximate value of these probabilities for $k = 25$. for $k = 50$.

REVIEW EXERCISES

1. In how many ways can one form subsets containing four elements from a set containing ten elements?

2. In how many ways can the officers, president, vice-president, and secretary, be selected from a class containing 217 members?

3. A certain automobile manufacturer makes four types of body designs, six choices of color, and four choices of interiors. How many different automobiles could be put together?

4. How many 7-digit telephone numbers are available if the telephone dial has ten positions, 1, 2, 3, 4, 5, 6, 7, 8, 9, 0?

5. How many automobile license plates can be assigned if the plate is to contain two letters followed by a four-digit number?

6. Use the binomial theorem to expand the product:

    (a) $(2 + n)^5$.   (b) $(1 - x^2)^3$.   (c) $(a + by)^6$.

7. Find the term of the product $(a + b)^{19}$ involving a^{13}.

8. In tossing pennies, what is the probability that in three tosses one gets two heads and one tails?

Suggested Readings

Fujii, J. N., *An Introduction to the Elements of Mathematics*, John Wiley, New York, 1961, Chs. 14, 15, pp. 230–260.

Richardson, M., *Fundamentals of Mathematics*, Macmillan, New York, 1958, Ch. 7, pp. 198–208.

General References

Allendoerfer, C. B., and C. O. Oakley, *Principles of Mathematics*, second edition, McGraw-Hill, New York, 1963, Ch. 12, pp. 402–446.

Cramer, Harald, *The Elements of Probability Theory*, John Wiley, New York, 1955.

Goldberg, S., *Probability*, Prentice-Hall, Englewood Cliffs, N. J., 1960.

Kemeny, J. G., J. L. Snell, and G. L. Thompson, *Introduction to Finite Mathematics*, Prentice-Hall, Englewood Cliffs, N. J., 1957, Chs. 3 and 4.

Mosteller, F., R. E. K. Rourke, and G. B. Thomas, Jr., *Probability with Statistical Applications*, Addison-Wesley, Reading, Mass., 1961.

Newman, James R., *The World of Mathematics*, Simon and Schuster, New York, 1956, Vol. II, Part IV.

Richardson, M., *Fundamentals of Mathematics*, Macmillan, New York, 1958, Ch. 13.

8 | MATHEMATICAL SYSTEMS

In this chapter we shall try to give several examples of small axiom systems, each of which illustrates the nature and structure of a mathematical theory. We will in each case begin by listing the undefined terms and stating the axioms. Then we shall develop a small part of the mathematics in each such system. If practicable, we shall point out several concrete realizations or applications of each abstract theory.

8–1 AN AXIOM SYSTEM

We begin by considering an axiom system in which the undefined terms are subclass and element of the class S. The undefined relation of belonging to a subclass is referred to by the phrases, "is a member of" and "is contained in." We have deliberately used class and subclass instead of set and subset because we wish to emphasize that, while this system can be thought of in the now familiar set language, the axioms of this system restrict rather drastically the properties of sets which subclasses and the class S of this axiom system possess. In this system, although the terminology sounds familiar, we must be on our guard to use only those properties of the undefined terms given in the axioms A_1 through A_7. We shall denote subclasses by $L, M, N, \ldots$, and elements of S by $a, b, c, \ldots$, and the relation of belonging to a subclass by $\in$.

A_1. If a and b are distinct elements of S, there is at least one subclass containing both a and b.

A_2. If a and b are distinct elements of S, there is not more than one subclass containing both a and b.

A_3.   Any two subclasses have at least one element of S in common.

A_4.   There exists at least one subclass.

A_5.   Every subclass contains at least three elements of S.

A_6.   All the elements of S do not belong to the same subclass.

A_7.   No subclass contains more than three elements of S.

Theorem 8–1.1

Every subclass contains exactly three elements of S.

Proof: Let L be any subclass.

1. L contains at least three elements of S.	A_5
2. L contains no more than three elements of S.	A_7
3. L contains exactly three elements of S.	1 and 2

Theorem 8–1.2

Any two subclasses have one and only one element of S in common.

Proof: Let L and M be any two subclasses.

1. There exists an element, say a, belonging to both L and M.	A_3
2. L and M have no common elements besides a.	A_2

Theorem 8–1.3

Any two elements a and b of S belong to one and only one subclass.

Proof

1. a and b belong to some subclass, say L.	A_1
2. a and b do not both belong to a subclass different from L.	A_2

Theorem 8–1.4

There are at least four elements of S.

Proof

1. There exists at least one subclass, say L.	A_4
2. L contains exactly three elements of S, a, b, c.	Th. 8–1.1
3. There exists an element d of S not in L.	A_6
4. There are at least four elements of S.	2 and 3

Theorem 8–1.5

There is more than one subclass.

Proof: Using the notation of the proof of Theorem 8–1.4:

1. $L = \{a, b, c\}$ is a subclass. $\qquad$ A$_4$, Th. 8–1.1
2. d is an element of S and $d \notin L$. $\qquad$ A$_6$
3. There exists a subclass M containing a and d. $\qquad$ A$_1$
4. $M \neq L$.† $\qquad$ $d \in M, d \notin L$

If we use the theorems which we have proved, we are able to collect the following information about subclasses.

1. Every subclass has exactly three elements.
2. There is more than one subclass.
3. Every pair of elements of S belongs to one and only one subclass.
4. Any two subclasses have one and only one element of S in common.

If we try to list as many subclasses as we can, we are led to the following list.

$L = \{a, b, c\}$

$M = \{a, d, e\}$ $\quad$ L and M can have one and only one element in common.

$N = \{b, d, f\}$ $\quad$ a cannot belong to another subclass containing b, c, d, or e, but b and d determine a unique subclass which cannot contain c or e.

$O = \{b, e, g\}$ $\quad$ b can belong only to a new subclass which does not contain a, c, d, or f.

$P = \{c, d, g\}$ $\quad$ c can belong only to a new subclass which does not

$Q = \{c, e, f\}$ $\quad$ contain a or b.

$R = \{f, a, g\}$ $\quad$ d cannot belong to another subclass containing a, b, c, e, f, or g; e cannot belong to another subclass containing a, b, c, d, f, or g.

Furthermore, it is easy to show that this list exhausts S. For suppose that there is an element, h of S, different from a, b, c, d, e, f, or g. By A$_1$, a and h belong to at least one subclass, T. But by A$_3$, T and N have an element in common. It cannot be b, since L and T would have

---

† Equality for two subclasses M and L is understood to mean that every element of M is an element of L and every element of L is an element of M.

both a and b in common. It cannot be d, since M and T would have both a and d in common. It cannot be f, since R and T would have both a and f in common. Hence there can be no elements of S besides $a, b, c, d, e, f,$ and g.

This mathematical theory has several realizations. If we interpret element of S as point in the plane, subclass as line in the plane, and belonging to a subclass as incidence (that is, a point is on a line, or a line contains a point), the axioms may be restated as:

A_1.   If a and b are two distinct points in the plane, there is at least one line passing through both a and b.

A_2.   There is not more than one line in the plane passing through any two distinct points.

A_3.   Any two lines have at least one point in common.

A_4.   There is at least one line in the plane.

A_5.   Every line contains at least three points.

A_6.   All the points in the plane do not lie on the same line.

A_7.   No line contains more than three points.

Figure 8–1 shows all essential features of the system. Note that this realization has point and line in their usual interpretation except for the line containing c, d, and g, which is not straight.

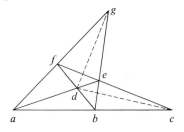

FIGURE 8–1

EXERCISES

1. Interpret "element of S" as "member of the city commission of a local government," "subclass" as a "committee composed of members of the commission," and "belongs to" as "is a member of." Rewrite the axioms A_1 through A_7 in this terminology.

2. Reinterpret Theorems 8–1.1 through 8–1.5 in this interpretation.

3. Show that there are three members of the commission who do not serve together on any committee.

4. Which of the three interpretations of this axiom system is more general? Why?

5. In what sense are all three systems the same?

8-2 GROUPS

Perhaps the simplest important mathematical system is a group.

Undefined terms:

"Set G."
"Element of G," denoted by "$a, b, c, \ldots$"
"Is an element of" or "belongs to," denoted by "$\in$."
"Operation," denoted by "$\circ$."

Axioms:

G_1. For any ordered pair of elements (a, b) belonging to G, $a \circ b$ is a unique element of G.　　　　　Closure Ax.

G_2. For every a, b, c belonging to G,

$$(a \circ b) \circ c = a \circ (b \circ c).$$　　　Associative Ax.

G_3. There exists an element $e \in G$, called the *identity* of G, such that for every element $a \in G$,

$$e \circ a = a \circ e = a.$$　　　Identity Ax.

G_4. For every element $a \in G$, there exists an element $a' \in G$, called the *inverse of a*, such that

$$a' \circ a = a \circ a' = e.$$　　　Inverse Ax.

Definition 8–2.1. A set G on which there is defined a binary operation "$\circ$" satisfying G_1, G_2, G_3, and G_4 is called a *group* (with respect to the operation "$\circ$").

Theorem 8–2.1

The identity element e of a group is unique.

Proof: Suppose that there are two elements e and e^* such that for all $a \in G$:

(i) $e \circ a = a \circ e = a.$
(ii) $e^* \circ a = a \circ e^* = a.$

1. $e \circ e^* = e^*.$	e^* for a in (i)
2. $e \circ e^* = e.$	e for a in (ii)
3. $e^* = e.$	1 and 2

Theorem 8–2.2

The inverse a' of an element a is unique.

Proof: Suppose a given element a has two inverses a' and a''.

1. $a'' \circ a = e$.	G_4
2. $(a'' \circ a) \circ a' = e \circ a'$.	1 and G_1
3. $a'' \circ (a \circ a') = a'$.	G_2 and G_3
4. $a'' \circ e = a'$.	G_4
5. $a'' = a'$.	G_3

Theorem 8–2.3

If $a \circ b = a \circ c$, then $b = c$ (Cancellation Law).

Proof

1. $a \circ b = a \circ c$.	Hypothesis
2. $a' \circ (a \circ b) = a' \circ (a \circ c)$.	1 and G_1
3. $(a' \circ a) \circ b = (a' \circ a) \circ c$.	G_2
4. $e \circ b = e \circ c$.	G_4
5. $b = c$.	G_3

Theorem 8–2.4

If a and b are any elements of G, $(a \circ b)' = b' \circ a'$.

Proof

1. $a', b', a \circ b$, and $(a \circ b)' \in G$.	G_1 and G_4
2. $(a \circ b) \circ (a \circ b)' = e$.	1 and G_4
3. $a' \circ [(a \circ b) \circ (a \circ b)'] = a' \circ e$.	1, 2, and G_1
4. $[a' \circ (a \circ b)] \circ (a \circ b)' = a'$.	G_2 and G_3
5. $[(a' \circ a) \circ b] \circ (a \circ b)' = a'$.	G_2
6. $(e \circ b) \circ (a \circ b)' = a'$.	G_4
7. $b \circ (a \circ b)' = a'$.	G_3
8. $b' \circ [b \circ (a \circ b)'] = b' \circ a'$.	1, 7, and G_1
9. $(b' \circ b) \circ (a \circ b)' = b' \circ a'$.	G_2
10. $e \circ (a \circ b)' = b' \circ a'$.	G_4
11. $(a \circ b)' = b' \circ a'$.	G_3

Definition 8–2.2. A group G is said to be *abelian* or *commutative* if for
    all a and $b \in G$, $a \circ b = b \circ a$.

A group is one of the simplest mathematical systems, since it involves
only one operation. We have already encountered many examples of
groups.

> EXAMPLE 8–2.1. The integers form a group with respect to
> the operation of addition.

G₁.   The sum of two integers is an integer.
G₂.   For any integers a, b, and c, $(a + b) + c = a + (b + c)$.
G₃.   The integer zero is the identity element of the group, since
       $0 + a = a + 0 = a$ for any integer a.
G₄.   The integer $-a$ serves as the inverse for the integer a, since
       $(-a) + a = a + (-a) = 0$.

Moreover, the integers under addition form an abelian group, since
$a + b = b + a$ for any integers a and b. Note that the natural numbers are not a group with respect to addition (no identity and no
inverses) or with respect to multiplication (no inverses except for 1).

> EXAMPLE 8–2.2. Consider the set of rotations of a square.

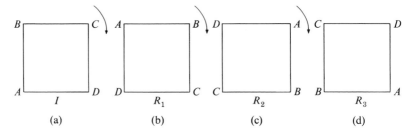

| (a) | (b) | (c) | (d) |

The elements of the set are the rotations I, R_1, R_2, R_3, where:
    I stands for a rotation through an angle of $0°$.
    R_1 stands for a clockwise rotation through an angle of $90°$.
    R_2 stands for a clockwise rotation through an angle of $180°$.
    R_3 stands for a clockwise rotation through an angle of $270°$.

The operation $\circ$ is following one rotation by another. In this case
$=$ means identity of position of the square.

To check G_1, we construct a "multiplication table."

∘	I	R_1	R_2	R_3
I	I	R_1	R_2	R_3
R_1	R_1	R_2	R_3	I
R_2	R_2	R_3	I	R_1
R_3	R_3	I	R_1	R_2

Hence the product of any two of the rotations is again one of these rotations. It is a tedious task to check that the associative axiom is satisfied for all triples (a, b, c). However, it can be shown that in general transformations of the plane are associative. The rotation through $0°$, I, serves as the identity. The inverses are:

$$I' = I.$$
$$R'_1 = R_3.$$
$$R'_2 = R_2.$$
$$R'_3 = R_1.$$

A check of the table shows that $a \circ b = b \circ a$ for all a and b in G, and therefore the group is abelian.

EXAMPLE 8–2.3.   The nonzero rational numbers form a group with respect to multiplication.

G_1.   The product of two nonzero rationals is again a nonzero rational.
G_2.   Multiplication of rational numbers is associative; $a(bc) = (ab)c$.
G_3.   1 serves as the identity; $a \cdot 1 = 1 \cdot a = a$ for any rational a.
G_4.   The inverse of $r \neq 0$ is $1/r$; $(1/r) \cdot r = r \cdot (1/r) = 1$.

In addition, $a \cdot b = b \cdot a$ for all rationals; hence the set of nonzero rationals forms an abelian group with respect to multiplication.

EXAMPLE 8–2.4.   Consider the permutations of the letters a, b, c. By a permutation, we mean a function whose domain is the set $\{a, b, c\}$ which has the entire set $\{a, b, c\}$ as its range.

There are $3 \cdot 2 \cdot 1 = 3!$ such permutations or functions. They are:

$$f_1 = \{(a, a), (b, b), (c, c)\}.$$
$$f_2 = \{(a, a), (b, c), (c, b)\}.$$
$$f_3 = \{(a, b), (b, a), (c, c)\}.$$
$$f_4 = \{(a, b), (b, c), (c, a)\}.$$
$$f_5 = \{(a, c), (b, b), (c, a)\}.$$
$$f_6 = \{(a, c), (b, a), (c, b)\}.$$

The elements of the set G which we wish to consider are the functions f_1, f_2, f_3, f_4, f_5, and f_6.

The operation is following one permutation by another; for functions in general, this operation is called "composition of functions." The symbol $=$ means equality for functions; i.e., the functions considered as sets of ordered pairs are equal.

To illustrate the group operation, suppose that $f = f_2 \circ f_3$.

$$f(x) = f_3[f_2(x)].$$
$$f(a) = f_3[f_2(a)] = f_3(a) = b.$$
$$f(b) = f_3[f_2(b)] = f_3(c) = c.$$
$$f(c) = f_3[f_2(c)] = f_3(b) = a.$$

Hence,

$$f_2 \circ f_3 = \{(a, b), (b, c), (c, a)\} = f_4.$$

Similarly,

$$f_1 \circ f_2 = \{(a, a), (b, c), (c, b)\} = f_2.$$

The group table is shown below.

$\circ$	f_1	f_2	f_3	f_4	f_5	f_6
f_1	f_1	f_2	f_3	f_4	f_5	f_6
f_2	f_2	f_1	f_4	f_3	f_6	f_5
f_3	f_3	f_6	f_1	f_5	f_4	f_2
f_4	f_4	f_5	f_2	f_6	f_3	f_1
f_5	f_5	f_4	f_6	f_2	f_1	f_3
f_6	f_6	f_3	f_5	f_1	f_2	f_4

1. Since only the functions f_1, f_2, f_3, f_4, f_5, and f_6 appear in the table, the set G is closed with respect to the operation of following one permutation by another (or the operation of composition of functions).

2. It can be checked that the associative axiom holds; for example,

$$(f_2 \circ f_3) \circ f_4 = f_2 \circ (f_3 \circ f_4).$$

From the table,

$$f_4 \circ f_4 = f_2 \circ f_5,$$
$$f_6 = f_6.$$

3. f_1 serves as the identity element.

4. $f_1' = f_1, f_2' \doteq f_2, f_3' = f_3, f_4' = f_6, f_5' = f_5, f_6' = f_4$. This is not an abelian group, since $f_2 \circ f_3 = f_4 \neq f_3 \circ f_2 = f_6$.

Example 8–2.4 is a special case of a very important class of groups: the so-called permutation groups. These are important, since every group with a finite number of elements is identical in structure to some permutation group.

EXERCISES

1. For each of the following sets, decide whether or not the set forms a group with respect to the indicated operation. (If not, why not?)

    (a) The set of natural numbers with respect to multiplication.
    (b) The set of even integers with respect to addition.
    (c) The set of integers with respect to multiplication.
    (d) The set of rational numbers with respect to addition.
    (e) $\{-1, 1\}$ with respect to multiplication.
    (f) $\{0, 1\}$ with respect to multiplication.
    (g) The set of all subsets of a given set with respect to $\cup$.
    (h) The set of all subsets of a given set with respect to $\cap$.
  *(i) The set of all linear functions with real coefficients with respect to $+$.

2. Which of the groups in Exercise 1 are abelian?

3. Let $\triangle ABC$ be an equilateral triangle. Let I, R_1, R_2 be clockwise rotations about the center of the triangle of $0°$, $120°$, and $240°$, respectively. Using Example 8–2.2 as a model, construct a "multiplication" table and decide whether or not these three rotations form a group.

4. In Example 8–2.4, check the associative axiom for the products, $f_2 \circ (f_5 \circ f_3)$, $f_3 \circ (f_4 \circ f_2)$, and $f_4 \circ (f_5 \circ f_6)$.

5. Taking the three elements f_1, f_4, and f_6 of Example 8–2.4, check to see whether they form a group with respect to the operation given.

$^+$6. A subset of a group which itself is a group with respect to the given operation is called a *subgroup*. Using the group of Example 8–2.4, find as many subgroups with two elements as you can. Are there any subgroups with four elements?

7. If a and b are elements of a group G, show that the equation $a \circ x = b$ has one and only one solution in G.

8. If a and b are elements of a group G, show that the equation $x \circ a = b$ has one and only one solution in G.

9. We define $a^1 = a$ and $a^2 = a \circ a$. Give a recursive definition for a^n, the nth power of a.

$^+$10. Show that for a group G with a finite number of elements, the subset consisting of the powers of a single element a form a subgroup of G. A group consisting of the powers of a single element a is called a *cyclic* group, and the element a is called a *generator* of the group.

11. Find the cyclic subgroup of the group G in Example 8–2.2 generated by R_2. (See Exercise 10 above.)

12. Do the even integers with respect to the operation of addition form a cyclic subgroup of the group of Example 8–2.1? If so, what is a generator of this subgroup? Is there more than one generator?

13. Does a cyclic group have to consist of a finite number of elements? Why?

14. Show that a group with three elements is abelian.

8–3 BOOLEAN ALGEBRA

Once again we return to the fundamental notion of set or class. We have seen that most of the mathematics which we have considered can be stated in set language. Even the important notion of a function can be formulated as a certain kind of set. So it is to the algebra of sets, or Boolean algebra, that we wish to return at this point. Most of the ideas and notation for the axiomatic statement of Boolean algebra have already been introduced, and it is a formal exposition of the structure of this part of mathematics which interests us in this section.

Boolean algebra had its origin in the attempt by the Englishman George Boole in his *An Investigation of the Laws of Thought* (1853) "... to investigate the fundamental laws of those operations of the mind by which reasoning is performed; to give expression to them in the symbolical language of a calculus, and upon this foundation to establish the science of logic and construct its method; to make that method itself the basis of a general method for the application of the mathematical doctrine of probabilities; and finally to collect from the various elements of truth brought to view in the course of these inquiries some probable intimations concerning the nature and constitution of the human mind."

The formulation which we give here is a more modern version of Boole's ideas. The undefined terms are again set, element, and belongs to.

Definition 8–3.1. A Boolean algebra is a set B on which two binary operations, $\cup$ and $\cap$, and an equivalence relation, $=$, are defined satisfying the following axioms:

B$_1$. For all $a, b \in B$,

$$a \cup b = b \cup a \quad \text{and} \quad a \cap b = b \cap a. \quad \text{Commutative Ax.}$$

B$_2$. There exist elements z and u corresponding to the operations $\cup$ and $\cap$, respectively, such that for all $a \in B$,

$$a \cup z = a \quad \text{and} \quad a \cap u = a \ (z \neq u). \quad \text{Identity Ax.}$$

B$_3$. For all $a, b, c \in B$,

$$a \cup (b \cap c) = (a \cup b) \cap (a \cup c),$$
and
$$a \cap (b \cup c) = (a \cap b) \cup (a \cap c). \quad \text{Distributive Ax.}$$

B$_4$. For every element $a \in B$, there exists an element $a' \in B$ such that

$$a \cup a' = u \quad \text{and} \quad a \cap a' = z. \quad \text{Complement Ax.}$$

Theorem 8–3.1. (*Principle of Duality*)

Any theorem of Boolean algebra remains valid if the operations $\cup$ and $\cap$ and the identity elements z and u are interchanged throughout. Any statement obtained from another statement by one application of the Principle of Duality is called the dual *of the first statement.*

Proof: This theorem about theorems follows directly from the axioms. We have only to note that interchanging the operations and identities in the set of axioms gives the same set of axioms back again. Consequently, any proof of a theorem may be turned into a proof of the dual by interchanging $\cup$ and $\cap$ and z and u in the statements constituting the proof of the original theorem.

This theorem is not peculiar to Boolean algebra. There are other mathematical systems in which the axioms are dual and which consequently contain a theorem similar to Theorem 8–3.1. The result of this theorem is that whenever we prove one theorem, we automatically have proved a second theorem, namely, its dual. Accordingly, theorems of Boolean algebra may be stated in pairs, and a proof need be given for only one member of the pair.

Theorem 8–3.2

For every $a \in B$, $\quad a \cup a = a \quad$ and $\quad a \cap a = a \quad$ (*Idempotent Property*).

Proof

1. $a \cup z = a$.	B_2
2. $a \cup (a \cap a') = a$.	B_4
3. $(a \cup a) \cap (a \cup a') = a$.	B_3
4. $(a \cup a) \cap u = a$.	B_4
5. $a \cup a = a$.	B_2

The proof for $a \cap a = a$ follows from Theorem 8–3.1. In the exercises the reader is asked to write out the details.

Theorem 8–3.3

For every $a \in B$, $a \cup u = u$ and $a \cap z = z$.

Proof

1. $a \cap a' = z$.	B_4
2. $a \cap (a' \cup z) = z$.	B_2
3. $(a \cap a') \cup (a \cap z) = z$.	B_3
4. $z \cup (a \cap z) = z$.	B_4
5. $(a \cap z) \cup z = z$.	B_1
6. $a \cap z = z$.	B_2

The proof of $a \cup u = u$ is left for the exercises.

Theorem 8–3.4

For all a, b ∈ B, a ∪ (a ∩ b) = a and a ∩ (a ∪ b) = a.

Proof

1. $a \cap u = a$. B_2
2. $a \cap (b \cup u) = a$.   Th. 8–3.3
3. $(a \cap b) \cup (a \cap u) = a$. B_3
4. $(a \cap b) \cup a = a$. B_2
5. $a \cup (a \cap b) = a$. B_1

$a \cap (a \cup b) = a$ follows by Theorem 8–3.1.

Theorem 8–3.5

In any Boolean algebra B, each of the operations ∪ and ∩ is associative; that is, for all a, b, c ∈ B, a ∪ (b ∪ c) = (a ∪ b) ∪ c and a ∩ (b ∩ c) = (a ∩ b) ∩ c.

The proof is left for the exercises.

Theorem 8–3.6

a′ is unique.

Proof: Suppose that there are two elements b and c satisfying B_4; that is,

$$a \cup b = u \wedge a \cap b = z \quad \text{and} \quad a \cup c = u \wedge a \cap c = z.$$

1. $b \cap u = b$. B_2
2. $b \cap (a \cup c) = b$. $a \cup c = u$
                                                     by hypothesis
3. $(b \cap a) \cup (b \cap c) = b$. B_3
4. $(a \cap b) \cup (b \cap c) = b$. B_1
5. $z \cup (b \cap c) = b$.   Hypothesis
6. $(b \cap c) \cup z = b$. B_1
7. $b \cap c = b$. B_2

Similarly, $c \cap b = c$, and hence

$$b \cap c = c. \qquad\qquad B_1$$

Therefore, since $b \cap c = b = c$, the inverse of a is unique.

Theorem 8–3.7

For any $b \in B$, $(b')' = b$.

Proof

    1. $b \cup b' = u$ and $b \cap b' = z$. B_4

    2. $b' \cup b = u$ and $b' \cap b = z$. B_1

Therefore, b satisfies the complement axiom B_4 for $a = b'$; i.e., b is the complement of $a = b'$. But the complement of a, $a' = (b')'$, is unique by Theorem 8–3.6. Therefore $(b')' = b$.

Theorem 8–3.8

For all $a, b \in B$, $(a \cap b)' = a' \cup b'$ and $(a \cup b)' = a' \cap b'$.

Proof

    1. $(a \cap b) \cup (a' \cup b')$

         $= (a' \cup b') \cup (a \cap b)$ B_1

    2. $= [(a' \cup b') \cup a] \cap [(a' \cup b') \cup b]$ B_3

    3. $= [(b' \cup a') \cup a] \cap [(a' \cup b') \cup b]$ B_1

    4. $= [b' \cup (a' \cup a)] \cap [a' \cup (b' \cup b)]$ Th. 8–3.5

    5. $= [b' \cup (a \cup a')] \cap [a' \cup (b \cup b')]$ B_1

    6. $= [b' \cup u] \cap [a' \cup u]$ B_4

    7. $= u \cap u$ Th. 8–3.3

    8. $= u$. B_2

    9. $(a \cap b) \cap (a' \cup b')$

         $= [(a \cap b) \cap a'] \cup [(a \cap b) \cap b']$ B_3

    10. $= [(b \cap a) \cap a'] \cup [(a \cap b) \cap b']$ B_1

    11. $= [b \cap (a \cap a')] \cup [a \cap (b \cap b')]$ Th. 8–3.5

    12. $= [b \cap z] \cup [a \cap z]$ B_4

    13. $= z \cup z$ Th. 8–3.3

    14. $= z$. B_2

Hence $a' \cup b'$ has the properties of the element a' in B_4, where $a \cap b$ replaces a. By Theorem 8–3.6 a' is unique; therefore, $(a \cap b)' = a' \cup b'$. By Theorem 8–3.1, $(a \cup b)' = a' \cap b'$ follows.

Definition 8–3.2. If $a, b \in B$, we say that $a \subset b$ if and only if $a \cup b = b$.

Theorem 8–3.9

For all $a \in B$, $a \subset a$.

Proof

> 1. $a \cup a = a$.   Th. 8–3.2
> 2. Therefore, $a \subset a$.   Def. 8–3.2

Theorem 8–3.10

If $a \subset b$ and $b \subset a$, then $a = b$.

Proof

> 1. $a \cup b = b$.   Hypothesis and Def. 8–3.2
> 2. $b \cup a = a$.   Hypothesis and Def. 8–3.2
> 3. $a \cup b = b \cup a$. B_1
> 4. Therefore, $b = a$.   Substitution of 1 and 2 into 3
> 5. $a = b$.   Symmetric property of $=$

This formal structure we have set forth in this section is an abstract mathematical theory. Any realization of this theory in which the undefined terms and axioms can be suitably interpreted is called a Boolean algebra. In particular, the algebra of sets is a Boolean algebra. If we interpret B to be the set of all subsets of a universal set U, then the elements of B are subsets of U. We interpret "is an element of," $\cup$,

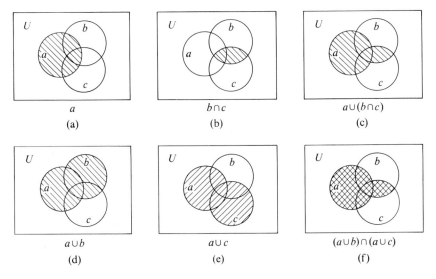

FIGURE 8–2

and $\cap$, in the usual way, as set membership, union, and intersection of sets. The equivalence relation $=$ is equality between sets. Then B_1 states that the operations of union and intersection are commutative; that is, if an element belongs either to set a or to set b, it belongs either to set b or to set a, and that if an element belongs both to set a and to set b, then it belongs both to set b and to set a. The null set serves as the identity element z for the operation union, and the universal set U serves as the identity element u for the operation intersection. Subsets of a universal set have the property that the operation $\cup$ distributes over $\cap$, as the Venn diagrams (Fig. 8–2) show.

Finally, for any set a, the set a' is the complement of a with respect to the set U. (We have previously denoted a' by $\bar{a}$.) Accordingly, the algebra of sets is a realization of the abstract mathematical system called Boolean algebra. In fact, it has been shown† that any Boolean algebra can be interpreted as an algebra of sets for some appropriately chosen universal set.

EXERCISES

1. Write in detail a proof for the second part of Theorem 8–3.2, that is, $a \cap a = a$.

2. Prove that $a \cup u = u$ for any element $a \in B$.

3. Prove that $a \cap (a \cup b) = a$ for all $a, b \in B$.

*4. To prove the associative property of $\cup$, proceed as follows: Let $a \cup (b \cup c) = x$ and $(a \cup b) \cup c = y$. We then wish to show that $x = y$.

Show: (i) $a \cap x = a$ and (ii) $a \cap y = a$. Therefore, $a \cap x = a \cap y$.

Then show:

    (iii) $a' \cap x = a' \cap (b \cup c)$ and (iv) $a' \cap y = a' \cap (b \cup c)$.

Therefore $a' \cap x = a' \cap y$.

    Then use

$$(a \cap x) \cup (a' \cap x) = (a \cap y) \cup (a' \cap x)$$

to show that $x = y$. The associative property of $\cap$ follows from Theorem 8–3.1.

5. Show that in any Boolean algebra, $z' = u$ and $u' = z$.

6. Prove that if $a \subset b$ and $b \subset c$, then $a \subset c$.

7. Show that $z \subset a \subset u$ for any element $a \in B$.

---

† M. H. Stone, "The Theory of Representations for Boolean Algebra," *Transactions of the American Mathematical Society*, Vol. 40, 1936, pp. 37–111.

8. Show that if $x \subset y$, then $x \subset (y \cup z)$ for any $z \in B$.

*9. Prove that $x \subset y$ if and only if $y' \subset x'$.

10. Use Venn diagrams to illustrate Theorem 8–3.8 for the algebra of sets.

11. Use Venn diagrams to illustrate that

$$a \cap (b \cup c) = (a \cap b) \cup (a \cap c).$$

*12. Show that the set $\{a, b, c, d\}$ with $\cup$ and $\cap$ defined by the following tables is a Boolean algebra.

$\cup$	a	b	c	d
a	a	b	c	d
b	b	b	b	b
c	c	b	c	b
d	d	b	b	d

$\cap$	a	b	c	d
a	a	a	a	a
b	a	b	c	d
c	a	c	c	a
d	a	d	a	d

8–4 THE BOOLEAN ALGEBRA $\{0, 1\}$

We now wish to examine other realizations of Boolean algebra which at first glance seem to have little in common with the algebra of sets. First, let us consider the set $\{0, 1\}$. Suppose that we interpret $\cup$ as $+$ and $\cap$ as $\times$ and define the operations of $+$ and $\times$ on the set $\{0, 1\}$ by the following "addition" and "multiplication" tables.

$+$	0	1
0	0	1
1	1	1

$\times$	0	1
0	0	0
1	0	1

Then one can check from the tables that B_1 is satisfied. B_2 holds for $z = 0$ and $u = 1$. B_3 can be verified by considering all possible cases (this is easy but extremely tedious); for example,

$$1 + (1 \times 1) = (1 + 1) \times (1 + 1),$$
$$1 + 1 = 1 \times 1,$$
$$1 = 1.$$

Axiom B_4 is satisfied if we take $0' = 1$ and $1' = 0$. Accordingly, this system forms a Boolean algebra. While its relation to an algebra of sets may not be apparent at this point, if we consider B to be the set consisting of the two elements $\emptyset$ and U, the null set and the universal set, and identify 0 with $\emptyset$ and 1 with U, then the two-element Boolean algebra $\{0, 1\}$ can be seen to be an algebra of sets.

This two-element Boolean algebra has two other interesting interpretations.

If we consider the logic of statements which we studied in Chapter 2, we may set up the following correspondence:

Boolean algebra $B = \{0, 1\}$	Logic
1	T
0	F
$+$	$\vee$
$\times$	$\wedge$
$'$	$\sim$
$=$	$\leftrightarrow$
$a, b, c, \ldots$	$p, q, r, \ldots$

We then assign to each statement the value 1 if it is true and the value 0 if it is false. It is easy to check that Axioms B_1 through B_4 are satisfied.

B_1. $p \vee q \leftrightarrow q \vee p$ and $p \wedge q \leftrightarrow q \wedge p$.

B_2. z stands for a sentence which is always false (a contradiction), and u stands for a sentence which is always true (a tautology).

B_3. To show that

$$a \vee (b \wedge c) \leftrightarrow (a \vee b) \wedge (a \vee c)$$

and

$$a \wedge (b \vee c) \leftrightarrow (a \wedge b) \vee (a \wedge c)$$

is left for the exercises.

B_4. $p \vee (\sim p)$ is always true, and $p \wedge (\sim p)$ is always false.

Second, if we consider an electrical network connecting two terminals T_1 and T_2, we may analyze this network as a Boolean algebra in the following way. Let $a, b, c, \ldots$ be switches in the network, and assign the value 0 to a switch if it is open and the value 1 to the switch if it is closed. We write $a + b$ if switches a and b are connected in parallel, and $a \times b$ if they are connected in series. Let a' be a switch which is open if a is closed and closed if a is open. Two networks joining T_1 and T_2 are said to be *equivalent* if for every possible state of the component switches, current passes through both, or does not pass through either. The two algebraic expressions representing the networks are said to be equal if the two networks are equivalent.

Parallel

Series

$B = \{0, 1\}$	Electrical networks
1	Switch closed
0	Switch open
+	Switches connected in parallel
×	Switches connected in series
'	Switch in opposite state
=	Equivalent networks
$a, b, c, \ldots$	Switches

B_1 states that:

is equivalent to

and that

$$T_1 — a — b — T_2 \quad \text{is equivalent to} \quad T_1 — b — a — T_2.$$

B_2 states that:

is equivalent to $T_1 — a — T_2$

(z is always open), and that

$$T_1 — a — u — T_2 \quad \text{is equivalent to} \quad T_1 — a — T_2$$

(u is always closed).

B_3 has the interpretation that the network:

is equivalent to the network

and that

$$T_1 \longrightarrow a \longrightarrow \boxed{\begin{array}{c} b \\ c \end{array}} \longrightarrow T_2$$

is equivalent to

$$T_1 \longrightarrow \boxed{\begin{array}{c} a - b \\ a - c \end{array}} \longrightarrow T_2.$$

B_4 asserts that if a' is a switch which is open when a is closed, and vice versa, then:

$$T_1 \longrightarrow \boxed{\begin{array}{c} a \\ a' \end{array}} \longrightarrow T_2 \quad \text{is always a closed circuit}$$

and that

$$T_1 \longrightarrow a \longrightarrow a' \longrightarrow T_2 \quad \text{is always open.}$$

This particular realization of the two-element Boolean algebra $\{0, 1\}$ has proved to be remarkably useful in the analysis and design of electrical networks. The theorems of Boolean algebra can be used to simplify complicated circuits, thereby decreasing the cost and increasing the reliability of a network. For example, the circuit represented by $(ab + c')' + a'c + b$ can be replaced by the equivalent circuit $b + c$, as the following argument shows.†

$$
\begin{aligned}
(ab + c')' + a'c + b &= (ab)'(c')' + a'c + b & \text{Th. 8–3.8} \\
&= (a' + b')c + a'c + b & \text{Th. 8–3.8 and 8–3.7} \\
&= c(a' + b') + a'c + b & B_1 \\
&= ca' + cb' + a'c + b & B_3 \\
&= ca' + ca' + cb' + b & B_1 \\
&= ca' + cb' + b & \text{Th. 8–3.2} \\
&= ca' + b + cb' & B_1 \\
&= ca' + (b + c)(b + b') & B_3 \\
&= ca' + (b + c)u & B_4 \\
&= ca' + (b + c) & B_2 \\
&= (b + c) + ca' & B_1 \\
&= b + (c + ca') & \text{Th. 8–3.5} \\
&= b + c. & \text{Th. 8–3.4}
\end{aligned}
$$

The other principal application of Boolean algebra to electrical networks is in the design of a network to accomplish a certain task. The so-called fundamental theorem of Boolean algebra allows one to

---

† $a \times b$ is written ab, as in ordinary multiplication.

construct an algebraic expression representing a network which will assume any desired state for the various states of the component switches. This expression can then be used to construct the required network.

EXERCISES

1. Check that $a + b = b + a$ and that $a \times b = b \times a$ for all pairs (a, b) in $B = \{0, 1\}$.

2. Verify that the two distributive properties of axiom B_3 hold in $B = \{0, 1\}$ for the triples

      (a) $(0, 1, 0)$,   (b) $(1, 0, 1)$,   (c) $(0, 0, 1)$.

3. Use truth tables to show that $p \vee q \leftrightarrow q \vee p$ is a tautology.

4. Give an example of a sentence which is always true. Give an example of a sentence which is always false. Is every sentence either always true or always false? What are the elements of the realization of Boolean algebra involving statements?

5. How are sets related to the Boolean algebra of statements?

6. Complete the following truth table to show that the statement $a \vee (b \wedge c) \leftrightarrow (a \vee b) \wedge (a \vee c)$ is a tautology.

a	b	c	a	$\vee$	$(b$	$\wedge$	$c)$	$\leftrightarrow$	$(a$	$\vee$	$b)$	$\wedge$	$(a$	$\vee$	$c)$
T	T	T													
T	T	F													
T	F	T													
T	F	F													
F	T	T													
F	T	F													
F	F	T													
F	F	F													
1	2	3	1	5	2	4	3	9	1	6	2	8	1	7	3

▲

7. Construct a truth table similar to the one in Exercise 6 to show that the statement $a \wedge (b \vee c) \leftrightarrow (a \wedge b) \vee (a \wedge c)$ is a tautology.

8. What is the interpretation of Theorem 8–3.7 in the algebra of statements?

9. What is the interpretation of Theorem 8–3.8 in the algebra of statements?

10. Draw a circuit which corresponds to the Boolean algebra expression:

    (a) $abc' + a'(b + c')$.   (b) $abc + ab(dc + ef)$.

    (c) $x[y(z + w) + z(u + v)]$.

11. Write the algebraic expression representing each of the following networks:

(a)

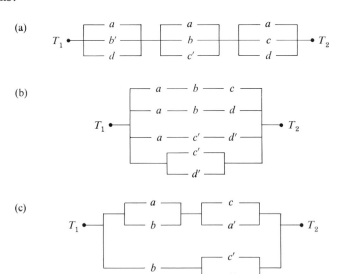

(b)

(c)

(d)

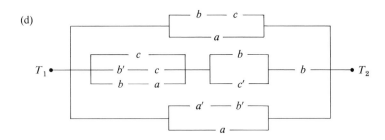

12. Simplify the expressions obtained in Exercise 11 by using the theory developed in Section 8-3, and draw the simplified circuit corresponding to the new algebraic expression.

8-5 FIELDS

In Chapter 3 we sketched briefly several extensions of the number system. However, with the exception of the natural numbers, we never really attempted to give a formal axiomatic development of any of the number systems. In this section we want to examine a mathematical system called a *field* and consider again the structure of some of the number systems in the light of this mathematical theory.

Definition 8–5.1. A field F is a set containing more than one element on which two binary operations $\oplus$ and $\boxdot$ are defined satisfying the following axioms:

F$_1$. F forms an abelian group with respect to $\oplus$.

F$_2$. $\{x \mid x \in F \wedge x \neq z, z$ is the identity for $\oplus\}$ forms an abelian group with respect to $\boxdot$.

F$_3$. For all $a, b, c \in F$, $a \boxdot (b \oplus c) = (a \boxdot b) \oplus (a \boxdot c)$.

A field is sometimes called a field of quotients, since by F$_1$, it is closed under addition, $\oplus$, and its inverse operation, subtraction ($a \ominus b$ means $a \oplus (-b)$, where $(-b)$ is the inverse of b with respect to $\oplus$); and by F$_2$ under multiplication, $\boxdot$, and its inverse operation division, ($a \oslash b$, means $a \boxdot b^{-1}$, where b^{-1} is the inverse of b with respect to $\boxdot$), with the exception that we do not divide by z (the identity with respect to $\oplus$).

Thus if we considered the set of numbers obtained by performing the operations $+$, $-$, $\times$, and $\div$ on the element 1, we are led to the field of rational numbers. We say that the rational field is *generated* by the number 1. Moreover, the rational field is the smallest field which contains the natural numbers.

Theorem 8–5.1

The rational numbers form a field if $\oplus$ is ordinary addition and $\boxdot$ ordinary multiplication.

The proof is left to the reader.

EXAMPLE 8–5.1. Is the set S generated by the numbers 1 and $\sqrt{2}$ a field?

Solution. Since 1 generates the rationals, the set generated by 1 and $\sqrt{2}$ contains all rational numbers. Since $\sqrt{2} \in S$, for any rational c/d, $(c/d)\sqrt{2} \in S$; in fact, all numbers of the form $a/b + (c/d)\sqrt{2} \in S$, where a, b, c, and d are integers, $bd \neq 0$. It can be shown that every element of S is of this form; that is,

$$S = \left\{ \frac{a}{b} + \frac{c}{d}\sqrt{2} \,\middle|\, a, b, c, d \in I \wedge bd \neq 0 \right\}.$$

(See Exercise 6 in the exercises.) It is easy to check that S satisfies the field axioms. (See Exercise 7.) This field S contains the rational numbers as a subset. A subset of a field, which is itself a field with respect to the same operations, is called a *subfield.* Thus the rationals are a subfield of any field containing the integer 1, in which $\oplus$ and $\boxdot$ are ordinary addition and multiplication, respectively.

There are, however, fields with only a finite number of elements.

EXAMPLE 8-5.2. Consider the set $\{0, 1, 2\}$, with $\oplus$ and $\boxdot$ defined by the following tables:

Table 1

$\oplus$	0	1	2
0	0	1	2
1	1	2	0
2	2	0	1

Table 2

$\boxdot$	0	1	2
0	0	0	0
1	0	1	2
2	0	2	1

F_1: Table 1 shows that G_1 is satisfied for $\oplus$.

F_2: The lower right-hand corner of Table 2 shows that $\{1, 2\}$ is closed with respect to $\boxdot$.

The associative axiom may be checked for both $\oplus$ and $\boxdot$.

0 is the identity for $\oplus$.
The inverses for $\oplus$ are

$-0 = 0$,
$-1 = 2$,
$-2 = 1$.

1 is the identity for $\boxdot$.
The inverses for $\boxdot$ are

$1^{-1} = 1$,
$2^{-1} = 2$.

F_3: There are 3^3 possible number triples (a, b, c), and F_3 can be checked for each possible case, e.g., for the triple $(1, 1, 1)$,

$$1 \boxdot (1 \oplus 1) = 1 \boxdot 2 = 2,$$

and

$$(1 \boxdot 1) \oplus (1 \boxdot 1) = 1 \oplus 1 = 2;$$

or for $(2, 2, 2)$

$$2 \boxdot (2 \oplus 2) = 2 \boxdot 1 = 2,$$

and

$$(2 \boxdot 2) \oplus (2 \boxdot 2) = 1 \oplus 1 = 2.$$

Since F_1, F_2, and F_3 are satisfied, $\{0, 1, 2\}$, with $\oplus$ and $\boxdot$ as defined above, is a field.

The rational field and the field S of Example 8–5.1 have two additional properties not shared by the finite field of Example 8–5.2. They satisfy the additional axioms:

F_4.　There exists a subset $P \subset F$ such that if $a \neq z$, the identity for the operation $\oplus$, then one and only one of a and $(-a)$ (the inverse of a with respect to $\oplus$) belongs to P.

F_5.　If $a \in P$ and $b \in P$, then $(a \oplus b) \in P$ and $(a \boxdot b) \in P$.

Definition 8–5.2. A field in which axioms F_4 and F_5 are satisfied is called an *ordered* field.

Both the field of rational numbers and the field of S of Example 8–5.1 are ordered fields. The subsets P of axiom F_4 are the set of positive rationals, and

$$\left\{\frac{a}{b} + \frac{c}{d}\sqrt{2} \,\middle|\, \frac{a}{b} + \frac{c}{d}\sqrt{2} \text{ is a positive real number}\right\},$$

respectively. The sum and product of two positive rationals are again positive rationals. Similarly, the sum and product of two positive real numbers of the form $a/b + (c/d)\sqrt{2}$ are again positive real numbers of the same form.

On the other hand, the finite field of Example 8–5.2 is not an ordered field. For suppose that $1 \in P$, then by F_5, $1 \oplus 1 = 2 \in P$. But 2 is the additive inverse of 1, and by F_4, not both 1 and $(-1) = 2$ can belong to P. If we suppose that $(-1) = 2 \in P$, we have the same difficulty. Both 2 and $2 \boxdot 2 = 1$ belong to P. But by F_4, both 2 and $(-2) = 1$ cannot belong to P. Since we have shown that it is impossible for one and only one of 1 and $(-1) = 2$ to belong to P, the finite field of Example 8–5.2 is not an ordered field.

The same sort of argument can be extended to show that no finite field is an ordered field.

In our discussion of extensions of the number system in Chapter 3, we indicated that the set of rational numbers was inadequate for finding exactly the lengths of all line segments. We were forced to include numbers like $\sqrt{2}$, π, etc., for this purpose. Again, in Chapter 5 we noted that these irrational numbers were limits of convergent sequences of rationals. For example, the sequence $1.4, 1.41, 1.414, \ldots, a_n, \ldots,$ where a_n is the rational approximation to the $\sqrt{2}$ containing n decimal places, has the limit $\sqrt{2}$ which is not in the field of rationals. In this sense the field of rationals is incomplete. *If we insisted that every convergent sequence of rational numbers have a limit in the number system, then the system would have to include all real numbers.* In this sense, the real numbers are the completion of the ordered field of rationals. The set of real numbers is a field. Mathematicians have shown that it is essentially the only complete ordered field. This number system is, in one way, the ultimate extension of the system of natural numbers. From this point on, any further extensions force us to sacrifice some property of the system we have so carefully built up.

One of the most useful extensions is the field of complex numbers. This is the field generated by the set $\{1, i\}$, where i is a number which has the property $i^2 = -1$. Since no real number has this property, the new system is truly an extension of the old. It can be shown that this system $C = \{a + bi \mid a, b$ are real numbers$\}$ is again a field, but it is impossible to order it in such a way that axioms F_4 and F_5 are satisfied. For if $i \in P$, if F_5 holds, $i \boxdot i = i^2 = -1 \in P$ and $(-1) \boxdot (-1) = 1 \in P$; but not both 1 and (-1) can belong to P by F_4. If $i \notin P$, then $-i \in P$ by F_4. But then $(-i) \boxdot (-i) = i^2 = -1 \in P$, and hence $(-1) \boxdot (-1) = 1 \in P$, and this also is impossible. This argument shows that the complex numbers cannot satisfy both F_4 and F_5, and hence do not form an ordered field.

The study of the structure of the real number system is a relatively recent development in mathematics. It is extremely gratifying to mathematicians to be able to see this most fundamental part of their discipline at last presented in an axiomatic development, the kind of development which sets forth so clearly the nature of mathematics and which is so characteristic of the work of mathematicians of the twentieth century.

EXERCISES

1. Which of the following sets are fields? If not, why not?
    (a) The integers with $\oplus$ and $\boxdot$ defined in the usual way.
    (b) $\{0, 1\}$ with $\oplus$ and $\boxdot$ as defined in Section 8–4.
    (c) $\{r \mid r = n/2^m$, where m is a natural number or zero and n is an integer$\}$ with $\oplus$ and $\boxdot$ defined in the usual way.
    (d) The set of all rationals with numerator 1.
    (e) The set of all real numbers formed from $\sqrt{3}$ by $+$, $-$, $\times$, and $\div$, with $\oplus$ and $\boxdot$ ordinary addition and multiplication, respectively.
    (f) The set of all polynomials.
    (g) $\{a + b\sqrt{5} \mid a$ and b rational numbers$\}$.

2. Give an informal argument for Theorem 8–5.1.

3. Does the set $\{0, 1\}$ form a field if we define $\oplus$ and $\boxed{\cdot}$ by the tables below.

$\oplus$	0	1
0	0	1
1	1	0

$\boxed{\cdot}$	0	1
0	0	0
1	0	1

Justify your answer.

$^+$4. A set R, on which two binary operations $\oplus$ and $\boxed{\cdot}$ are defined, which has the following properties:

(a) F_1 and F_3 are satisfied
(b) R is closed with respect to $\boxed{\cdot}$, that is

$$a, b, \in R \rightarrow a \boxed{\cdot} b \in R$$

(c) $\boxed{\cdot}$ is associative, that is

$$a, b, c \in R \rightarrow a \boxed{\cdot} (b \boxed{\cdot} c) = (a \boxed{\cdot} b) \boxed{\cdot} c$$

is called a *ring*. Which of the following sets are rings?

(i) $\{x + y\sqrt{2} \mid x, y \in I\}$, with $\oplus$ and $\boxed{\cdot}$ ordinary addition and multiplication, respectively.
(ii) $\{0, 1\}$, with $\oplus$ and $\boxed{\cdot}$ as defined in Exercise 3.
(iii) The even integers, with $\oplus$ and $\boxed{\cdot}$ defined in the usual way.
(iv) The odd integers, with $\oplus$ and $\boxed{\cdot}$ defined in the usual way.

*5. Try to devise "addition" and "multiplication" tables for the set $\{0, 1, 2, 3, 4\}$ so as to form a field.

6. Show that the sum, difference, product, and quotient of two numbers of the form $a/b + (c/d)\sqrt{2}$, a, b, c, d integers with $bd \neq 0$, are again of this form.

7. Check axioms F_1 and F_2 for the set of Example 8–5.1.

8. Is the set $\{x, y\}$, with $\oplus$ and $\boxed{\cdot}$ defined by the following tables, a field?

$\oplus$	x	y
x	x	y
y	y	x

$\boxed{\cdot}$	x	y
x	x	x
y	x	y

9. Prove that in a field $(a \oplus b) \boxed{\cdot} c = (a \boxed{\cdot} c) \oplus (b \boxed{\cdot} c)$.

$^+$10. In an ordered field, we define $a \otimes b$ to mean $b \oplus (-a) \in P$. Prove that in an ordered field $a \otimes b \wedge b \otimes c \rightarrow a \otimes c$.

$^+$11. In an ordered field, show that $a \otimes b \rightarrow a \oplus c \otimes b \oplus c$.

12. Define $|a|$ in any ordered field.

8-6 CONCLUSION

In this chapter we have looked at several abstract mathematical systems. In each case the system consisted of a set of axioms stating properties which certain undefined terms were assumed to have, definitions, and theorems. The theorems invariably could be made to assume the form, "If p, then q." We are now in a better position to understand Bertrand Russell's remark about the nature of mathematics. In these abstract systems, it is true that we do not know *what* we are talking about (no attempt was made to define the undefined terms!), and, moreover, the theorems never claim that any statement p is "true"; they merely state that if we assume p, then q follows. Therefore, if mathematics consists of abstract structures of the kind seen in this chapter, Russell's statement, ". . . mathematics may be defined as the subject in which we never know what we are talking about, nor whether what we are saying is true," would seem to have a certain validity.

Of course, mathematics was not always seen in this light. In fact, until shortly before the twentieth century most mathematicians would not have entertained any such idea about the nature of mathematics.

The concrete realizations of mathematical systems and the application of mathematical results to practical problems would have seemed to many to be a more acceptable description of mathematics.

These remarks serve only to point up the fact that mathematics is a changing, growing, living part of the intellectual life of man. At different times in history, it has been cultivated for various purposes and pursued from various points of view. Much of the work which was once the main preoccupation of mathematicians is now a part of the training of every child in school and is no longer of interest to mathematicians. A large part of the work of mathematicians of other days would now be called astronomy or physics or even astrology and theology. Hence rather than to try to define what mathematics is, we are led to try to look at what mathematicians are doing and to try to understand how they view their work. This is as close as we can come to defining the part of our intellectual heritage called mathematics. In the middle of the twentieth century, mathematics seems to be the study of abstract structures and the relations between them. The importance of this endeavor is apparent in the many ways in which mathematics and its applications have changed the lives and thoughts of men.

Suggested Readings

ALLENDOERFER, C. B., and C. O. OAKLEY, *Principles of Mathematics*, second edition, McGraw-Hill, New York, 1963, Chs. 2, 4, 13.

EVENSON, A. B., *Modern Mathematics*, Scott, Foresman and Co., Chicago, 1962, Ch. 8 (Groups and Fields), pp. 165–190.

HAFSTROM, J. E., *Basic Concepts in Modern Mathematics*, Addison-Wesley, Reading, Mass., 1961, Ch. 5 (Groups), pp. 69–82.

HOHN, FRANZ E., "Some Mathematical Aspects of Switching" in the *American Mathematical Monthly*, Vol. 62 (1955), pp. 75–90.

LUCE, R. D., "Studies in Mathematics," in *Some Basic Mathematical Concepts*, Vol. I, School Mathematics Study Group, Yale University, New Haven, Conn., 1959, Ch. 4 (Boolean Algebra), pp. 139–161.

STABLER, E. R., "Boolean Algebras as an Introduction to Postulational Methods," in the *American Mathematical Monthly*, Vol. 50 (1943), pp. 106–110.

General References

BELL, E. T., *Men of Mathematics*, Simon and Schuster, New York, 1937, Ch. 23 (Boole).

EXNER, R. M. and M. F. ROSSKOPF, *Logic in Elementary Mathematics*, McGraw-Hill, New York, 1959, Ch. 4, pp. 100–125.

HOHN, FRANZ E., *Applied Boolean Algebra*, Macmillan, New York, 1960.

MAY, K. O., *Elements of Mathematics*, Addison-Wesley, Reading, Mass., 1959, Ch. 10.

STABLER, E. R., *An Introduction to Mathematical Thought*, Addison-Wesley, Reading, Mass., 1953, Ch. 7 (Finite Geometry), pp. 139–145; Ch. 9 (Groups, Rings, and Boolean Algebra), pp. 175–210.

STOLL, R. R., *Sets, Logic and Axiomatic Theories*, Freeman, San Francisco, 1961.

BIBLIOGRAPHY

ALLENDOERFER, C. B., and C. O. OAKLEY, *Principles of Mathematics*, second edition, McGraw-Hill, New York, 1963.

BELL, E. T., *Men of Mathematics*, Simon and Schuster, New York, 1937.

BELL, E. T., *The Development of Mathematics*, McGraw-Hill, New York, 1945.

COURANT, R., and H. E. ROBBINS, *What Is Mathematics?*, Oxford University Press, New York, 1941.

DANTZIG, T., *Number: The Language of Science*, Doubleday, Garden City, N. Y., 1956.

DUBISCH, R., *The Nature of Number*, The Ronald Press, New York, 1952.

EVENSON, A. B., *Modern Mathematics*, Scott, Foresman and Co., Chicago, 1962.

FÉLIX, L., *The Modern Aspect of Mathematics*, Basic Books, Inc., New York, 1960.

FUJII, J. N., *An Introduction to the Elements of Mathematics*, John Wiley, New York, 1961.

KASNER, E., and J. NEWMAN, *Mathematics and the Imagination*, Simon and Schuster, New York, 1940.

KEMENY, J. G., J. L. SNELL, and G. L. THOMPSON, *Introduction to Finite Mathematics*, Prentice-Hall, Englewood Cliffs, N. J., 1957.

KLINE, M., *Mathematics in Western Culture*, Oxford University Press, New York, 1953.

KRAMER, E., *The Main Stream of Mathematics*, Oxford University Press, New York, 1951.

LIEBER, L. R., *The Education of T. C. Mits*, Norton, New York, 1942.

LOGSDON, M. I., *A Mathematician Explains*, University of Chicago Press, Chicago, 1935.

National Council of Teachers of Mathematics, *Insights into Modern Mathematics*, Twenty-third Yearbook, NCTM, Washington, 1957.

NEWMAN, J. R., *The World of Mathematics*, Simon and Schuster, New York, 1956.

PETER, ROZSA, *Playing with Infinity*, Simon and Schuster, New York, 1962.

RADEMACHER, H., and O. TOEPLITZ, *The Enjoyment of Mathematics*, Princeton University Press, Princeton, N. J., 1957.

RICHARDSON, M., *Fundamentals of Mathematics*, Macmillan, New York, 1958.

SANFORD, V., *A Short History of Mathematics*, Houghton Mifflin, New York, 1930.

SINGH, J., *Modern Mathematics*, Dover, New York, 1959.

STOLL, R. R., *Sets, Logic and Axiomatic Theories*, Freeman, San Francisco, 1961.

STRUIK, D. J., *A Concise History of Mathematics*, Dover, New York, 1948.

TITCHMARSH, E. C., *Mathematics for the General Reader*, Doubleday Anchor Books, Garden City, N. Y., 1959.

LIST OF SYMBOLS

CHAPTER 1. Sets

$\{\ \}$	set 4
$\{x \mid \ldots\}$	the set of x's such that . . . 4
U	the universal set 4
$\emptyset$	the empty set (the null set) 4
$\in$	belongs to or is a member of 5
$\notin$	does not belong to 5
$=$	equality 7
$\subset$	is a subset of, is contained in 7
$\neq$	is not equal to 8
$\cap$	intersection 8
$\cup$	union 8
$\overline{A}$	complement of set A 9
$\subseteq$	subset 10

CHAPTER 2. Mathematics and Logic

$\sim$	negation 20
$\wedge$	conjunction 20
$\vee$	disjunction 20
$\underline{\vee}$	exclusive disjunction 21
$p \to q$	conditional; if p, then q; p implies q 24
$\leftrightarrow$	biconditional; if and only if 26
$\forall$	universal quantifier; for all 42
$\exists$	existential quantifier; there exists 42

CHAPTER 3. Sets of Numbers

n'	the successor of n 47
$n!$	n factorial 51
(a, b)	ordered pair 52
$<$	less than 53
$(A \mid \overline{A})$	Dedekind cut 62
$\geq$	greater than or equal to 62
$>$	greater than 63

CHAPTER 4. Relations and Functions

$A \times B$	cartesian product of sets A and B 67
$a \, \rho \, b$	a is in the relation ρ to b 69

$f = \{(x, y)\}$ function   76

$f(x)$ a value of the function f, second member of the ordered pair $(x, y) \in f$ 77

(x, y) coordinates of the point P 80

I identity function $\{(x, x)\}$ 80

$|x|$ absolute value   81

$[x]$ greatest integer   81

$\leq$ is less than or equal to   81

$\sqrt{x}$ square root   82

$\rho*$ converse of the relation ρ 84

f^{-1} inverse function of the function f 84

$\overline{P_1 P_2}$ line segment joining P_1 and P_2 88

m slope of line   89

CHAPTER 5. Sequences and Limits

s_n nth term of a sequence   95

$\lim_{n \to \infty} s_n$ limit of a sequence   100

$1.\overline{41}$ repeating decimal 1.414141 . . .   105

$]a, b[$ open interval from a to b 107

$[a, b]$ closed interval from a to b 107

$\lim_{x \to a} f(x)$ limit of function f at a 108

CHAPTER 6. The Calculus

f', Df derivative of the function f 116

$\Delta x, \Delta y$ increments   120

$\lim_{\Delta x \to 0} (\Delta y / \Delta x)$ rate of change of y with respect to x (derivative)   120

f'' derivative of the function Df 126

$\underline{S}_n$ lower sum   128

$\overline{S}_n$ upper sum   129

$\sum_{i=1}^{n} a_i$ $a_1 + a_2 + \cdots + a_n$ 129

$\int_a^b f(x)\, dx$ the definite integral of f over the interval $[a, b]$ 132

$\int_a^b f$ the definite integral of f over the interval $[a, b]$ 132

$a \not< b$ a is not less than b 132

CHAPTER 7. Counting and Probability

P_r^n number of permutations of n things taken r at a time   144

$\binom{n}{r}$ the number of combinations of n things taken   145 r at a time, binomial coefficient of $a^{n-r}b^r$ in $(a + b)^n$ 148

C_r^n number of combinations of n things taken r at a time   145

$P = \{(X, P(X))\}$ probability function   150

CHAPTER 8. Mathematical Systems

$\circ$ group operation   160

e identity element of a group   160

a' inverse of element a in a group   160

z identity element for $\cup$ in Boolean algebra   167

u identity element for $\cap$ in Boolean algebra   167

a' complement of element a in Boolean algebra   167

$\oplus$ operation of addition in a field   179

$\boxed{\cdot}$ operation of multiplication in a field   179

z the identity element for $\oplus$ in a field   179

$-a$ the inverse of a with respect to $\oplus$ 179

a^{-1} the inverse of a with respect to $\boxed{\cdot}$ 179

GREEK LETTERS

Δ	δ	delta
	ϵ	epsilon
	π	pi
	ρ	rho
Σ		sigma

ANSWERS TO SELECTED EXERCISES

CHAPTER 1
Section 1–1

1. (a) α, β, γ (c) Switzerland, Red China, Monaco, Germany
(e) 0, 1, 2 (any real number)   (g) There are none.
(i) 2, -2 (k) New York, New Jersey, Michigan

3. $\{0, 1\}$

5. No. The set containing the two numbers 1 and 2 is not an element of the given set. The numbers 1 and 2, however, are members of the given set.

7. No. Yes.   9. They all have 3 members.

11. (a) The set of all positive integers less than 6.   (c) The first 6 terms of the arithmetic progression with first term 2 and common difference 4.   (e) The set of all states of the U.S. whose names begin with the letter M.

Section 1–2

1. (a) F   (c) F   (e) T

+3. (a) $\emptyset$, $\{1\}$, $\{2\}$, $\{3\}$, $\{1, 2\}$, $\{1, 3\}$, $\{2, 3\}$, $\{1, 2, 3\}$;
(c) $\emptyset$, $\{0\}$, $\{\{1\}\}$, $\{0, \{1\}\}$. 2^n

5. (a) No   (c) Yes   (e) Yes

+9. (a) E is the set of all odd natural numbers.   (c) The set of composite numbers and 1   (e) $\{2\}$ (g) $\{\overline{2}\}$

11. $U, \emptyset, A, A, \emptyset$

Section 1–3

1. (a) 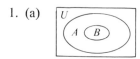   (c)

(e)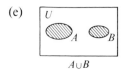

$A \cup B$

(g)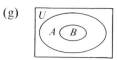

192

3. (a) 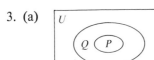 (c)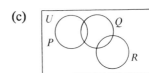

5. Let P be the positive integers, I, the integers, Q, the rational numbers, and R, the real numbers.

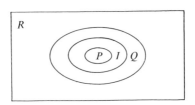

7. (a)

$A \cup B$

$A \cap \bar{B}$

$(A \cap \bar{B}) \cup B$

(c)

$A \cap B$

$A \cap \bar{B}$

$(A \cap B) \cup (A \cap \bar{B})$

Section 1–4

1. (a) Finite   (c) Finite   (e) Finite (probably)

3. (a) Yes.

$$\begin{array}{ccccc} 1 & 2 & 3 & n & 20 \\ \updownarrow & \updownarrow & \updownarrow \cdots \updownarrow \cdots & \updownarrow \\ 2 & 4 & 6 & 2n & 40 \end{array}$$

(c) Yes.

$$\begin{array}{cccc} 1 & 2 & 3 & n \\ \updownarrow & \updownarrow & \updownarrow \cdots & \updownarrow \\ 1 & 3 & 5 & 2n-1 \end{array}$$

*(e) Yes.

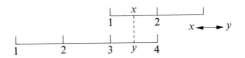

5. (a) Equivalent and equal   (c) Neither

Review Exercises

1. $1 \in N$; $1, -3, 0 \in I$; $1, \frac{2}{3}, -3, 0, \frac{17}{19} \in Q$; all belong to R.

3. (a) F   (c) T   (e) T

5. (a) $\{0\}$ (c) $\{1, 2, 3\}$ (e) $\{0, 1, 2, 3, 5, 6, 7,\}$

7. (a) $\overline{A}$ (c) $\overline{A} \cap C$

9. (a)   (c)   (e)

$A \cup \overline{B}$

$\overline{A} \cup \overline{B}$

$\overline{A \cap B}$

CHAPTER 2

Section 2–1

1. (a) $2 \neq 1 + 3$.
(c) $2 = 1 + 3$ and 3 is greater than 0.
(e) $2 \leq 3$ and $3 > 0$

3. (a)

$\sim$	$(p$	$\vee$	$q)$
F	T	T	T
F	T	T	F
F	F	T	T
T	F	F	F
▲			

(c)

$\sim$	$(p$	$\vee$	$q)$	$\wedge$	p
F	T	T	T	F	T
F	T	T	F	F	T
F	F	T	T	F	F
T	F	F	F	F	F
4	1	3	2	5	1
				▲	

5. (a) Ice is not cold. (c) Some Russians are not communists *or* Not all Russians are communists. (e) There are not 30 days in September.

7. (a)

p	$\sim$	$(\sim$	$p)$
T	T	F	T
F	F	T	F
	▲	▲	

(c)

$\sim$	$(p$	$\vee$	$q)$	$\sim$	p	$\wedge$	$\sim$	q
F	T	T	T	F	T	F	F	T
F	T	T	F	F	T	F	T	F
F	F	T	T	T	F	F	F	T
T	F	F	F	T	F	T	T	F
		▲				▲		

9. $\sim(\sim p \wedge \sim q)$ equivalent to $p \vee q$. This statement is true if either John or Jim passed the test.

Section 2–2

1. (a) *p:* 5 is an even integer.
   q: 15 is divisible by 6.
   $$p \rightarrow q$$

   (e) *p:* The man in the moon is real.
   q: Santa Claus is real.
   r: Many kiddies are deceived.
   $$\sim p \wedge (\sim q \rightarrow r)$$

   (c) *p:* New York City is north of St. Louis.
   q: The population of Chicago is larger than that of New York City.
   $$p \rightarrow q$$

   (a) True   (b) True   (d) True   (e) True

3.

(a)

$(p$	$\rightarrow$	$p)$	$\vee$	$(p$	$\rightarrow$	$\sim$	$p)$
T	*T*	*T*	*T*	*T*	*F*	*F*	*T*
F	*T*	*F*	*T*	*F*	*T*	*T*	*F*
1	2	1	5	1	4	3	1

▲

(c)

$(q$	$\rightarrow$	$p)$	$\leftrightarrow$	$(\sim$	q	$\vee$	$p)$
T	*T*	*T*	*T*	*F*	*T*	*T*	*T*
T	*F*	*F*	*T*	*F*	*T*	*F*	*F*
F	*T*	*T*	*T*	*T*	*F*	*T*	*T*
F	*T*	*F*	*T*	*T*	*F*	*T*	*F*
1	3	2	6	4	1	5	2

▲

⁺5.

$\sim$	$(p$	$\rightarrow$	$q)$	$\leftrightarrow$	$(p$	$\wedge$	$\sim$	$q)$
F	*T*	*T*	*T*	*T*	*T*	*F*	*F*	*T*
T	*T*	*F*	*F*	*T*	*T*	*T*	*T*	*F*
F	*F*	*T*	*T*	*T*	*F*	*F*	*F*	*T*
F	*F*	*T*	*F*	*T*	*F*	*F*	*T*	*F*
4	1	3	2	7	1	6	5	2

▲

7.

	Statement	Converse	Inverse	Contrapositive
(a)	$q \rightarrow p$	$p \rightarrow q$	$\sim q \rightarrow \sim p$	$\sim p \rightarrow \sim q$
(b)	$\sim p \rightarrow \sim q$	$\sim q \rightarrow \sim p$	$p \rightarrow q$	$q \rightarrow p$
(c)	$\sim q \rightarrow p$	$p \rightarrow \sim q$	$q \rightarrow \sim p$	$\sim p \rightarrow q$
(d)	$p \rightarrow \sim q$	$\sim q \rightarrow p$	$\sim p \rightarrow q$	$q \rightarrow \sim p$
(e)	$\sim q \rightarrow \sim p$	$\sim p \rightarrow \sim q$	$q \rightarrow p$	$p \rightarrow q$

9.
p: Triangle *ABC* is isosceles.
q: Triangle *ABC* is equilateral.

11.

$\sim$	$(p$	$\leftrightarrow$	$q)$	$\leftrightarrow$	$(p$	$\leftrightarrow$	$\sim$	$q)$
F	*T*	*T*	*T*	*T*	*T*	*F*	*F*	*T*
T	*T*	*F*	*F*	*T*	*T*	*T*	*T*	*F*
T	*F*	*F*	*T*	*T*	*F*	*T*	*F*	*T*
F	*F*	*T*	*F*	*T*	*F*	*F*	*T*	*F*
4	1	3	2	7	1	6	5	2

▲

Section 2–4

1.

$[(p$	$\rightarrow$	$q)$	$\wedge$	$p]$	$\rightarrow$	q
T	T	T	T	T	T	T
T	F	F	F	T	T	F
F	T	T	F	F	T	T
F	T	F	F	F	T	F
1	3	2	4	1	5	2

▲

+3.

$[(p$	$\rightarrow$	$q)$	$\wedge$	$\sim$	$q]$	$\rightarrow$	$\sim$	p
T	T	T	F	F	T	T	F	T
T	F	F	F	T	F	T	F	T
F	T	T	F	F	T	T	T	F
F	T	F	T	T	F	T	T	F
1	3	2	5	4	2	7	6	1

▲

+5.

p	$\wedge$	$\sim$	p
T	F	F	T
F	F	T	F

▲

Section 2–5

3. (a) $x = 0$

(c) $c = 0, a = 1, b = 2$

(e) $a = 2, b = -3$

(g) 2 is a prime.

Section 2–6

1. (a) Some integers are not rational numbers.

(c) All members of the ACLU are Socialists.

(e) There is at least one integer which is less than or equal to one.

3. (a) Some animals are not carnivorous or some birds are not vegetarians.

(c) There are some writings of philosophers which are neither ambiguous nor unintelligible.

(e) There is a real number such that its square is nonpositive and it is not zero.

Review Exercises

1. (a) F   (c) T   (e) F.

3. Converse: If a man follows the party line, the Communists approve of him.

Original statement: That a man follow the party line is a necessary condition for the Communists to approve of him.

5. No. Getting a raise was a necessary but not sufficient condition for the marriage.

7. To prove that $B \subset \overline{A}$ we must prove that any element of B is also an element of $\overline{A}$. Suppose $b \in B$. Since A and B are disjoint, $b \notin A$. Therefore $b \in \overline{A}$, since every element belongs either to A or to $\overline{A}$. Since b was chosen to be any element belonging to B, we have shown that any element belonging to B belongs to $\overline{A}$.

9. An *axiom* is a statement which is assumed to have the logical label "true" in a given mathematical system. It is a basic statement which describes properties of, or relations between, the undefined terms.

A *definition* is an agreement as to how a new word shall be used.
A *theorem* is a statement which is to be deduced from the axioms and definitions of the mathematical system.

CHAPTER 3

Section 3–1

1. (a) 3   (c) 10   (e) 10   3. (a) $2 + 1 = 2' = 3$

$$
\begin{aligned}
\text{(c)} \ 4 \cdot 2 + 2 &= 4 \cdot 1' + 1' \\
&= (4 \cdot 1 + 4) + 1' \\
&= [(4 \cdot 1 + 4) + 1]' \\
&= [(4 + 4) + 1]' \\
&= [(4 + 4)']' \\
&= (4 + 3')'' \\
&= (4 + 3)''' \\
&= (4 + 2')''' \\
&= (4 + 2)'''' \\
&= 6'''' \qquad \text{(by an example in text)} \\
&= 10
\end{aligned}
$$

$$
\begin{aligned}
\text{(e)} \ (5 \cdot 2' + 3)' &= [(5 \cdot 2 + 5) + 3]' \\
&= [(5 \cdot 1' + 5) + 3]' \\
&= [(\{5 \cdot 1 + 5\} + 5) + 3]' \\
&= [(\{5 + 5\} + 5) + 3]' \\
&\quad \text{etc.}
\end{aligned}
$$

Section 3–2

*9. (a) The statement is false when $n = 1$.

(c) The statement is false when $n = 1$.

Section 3–3

1. (b) 1   (c) 2   3.

N	Z	P

I

5. 4

7. No. There are integers which are not natural numbers.

Section 3–4

[+]1. ad, bc, and bd are integers since the set of integers is closed under multiplication. $ad + bc$ is an integer since the set of integers is closed under addition. Therefore $(ad + bc)/bd$ is a rational number, since it is the quotient of two integers.

(a) $\frac{46}{35} = 1\frac{11}{35}$ (c) $\frac{25}{39}$

[+]3. By problem 2, $\dfrac{-1}{1} \cdot \dfrac{c}{d} = -\dfrac{c}{d}$ is rational. $\dfrac{a}{b} + \left(-\dfrac{c}{d}\right)$ is rational

since, by problem 1, the sum of 2 rational numbers is rational.

(a) $\frac{4}{3} = 1\frac{1}{3}$ (c) $\frac{44}{15} = 2\frac{14}{15}$

[+]5. $\dfrac{a}{b} = (a, b)$ and $\dfrac{ac}{bc} = (ac, bc)$; $a \cdot bc = b \cdot ac$; so $(a, b) = (ac, bc)$.

Therefore

$$\frac{a}{b} = \frac{ac}{bc}.$$

(a) $2 \cdot 12 = 4 \cdot 6$ (c) $17 \cdot 90 = 30 \cdot 51$

7. $2 \cdot 4 = 8 < 3 \cdot 3 = 9$

*9. Given any 2 positive rationals a and b. Suppose $a < b$. Then $2a < a + b$, since $a < b$. Therefore

$$a < \frac{a + b}{2}.$$

Likewise $a + b < 2b$, since $a < b$. Therefore

$$\frac{a + b}{2} < b.$$

Thus

$$a < \frac{a + b}{2} < b.$$

Section 3–5

1. $-\sqrt{2}, \pi, e$ 3. $A = \{r \mid r^2 < 3 \lor r \leq 0\}$

*5. Yes. Yes.

Review Exercises

1. $3 + 2 = 3 + 1'$ $4 + 1 = 4'$
            $= (3 + 1)'$ $= 5$
            $= 3''$
            $= 4'$
            $= 5$

3. In a proof by induction we let S be the set of natural numbers for which the theorem is true. We then show that S has two properties: (i) $1 \in S$; (ii) $k \in S \rightarrow (k + 1) \in S$. However, by axiom P_5 any set which possesses these two properties is the set of all natural numbers. Hence the set S of natural numbers for which the theorem is true is the set of all natural numbers by axiom P_5.

5. (a) 1   (c) 0

7. $\frac{2}{5}, \frac{9}{20}, \frac{12}{25}$ or $\frac{9}{24}, \frac{5}{12}, \frac{11}{24}$ 9. $A = \{r \mid r^2 < 5 \lor r \leq 0\}$

CHAPTER 4

Section 4–1

1. (a) $A \times B = \{(a, a), (a, b)\}$
(c) $B \times F = \{(a, 2), (a, 4), (b, 2), (b, 4)\}$
(e) $E \times F = \{(2, 2), (2, 4), (4, 2), (4, 4), (6, 2), (6, 4)\}$

3. $\{(1, 5), (2, 6), (3, 7)\}$; $\{(1, 5), (1, 7)\}$; $\{(2, 6), (2, 7), (3, 6), (3, 7)\}$ (any 3 subsets of $A \times B$)

5. Yes. Yes.

7. Yes, because $A \times B \subset U \times U$.

9. No.

+11. (i) Not reflexive, not symmetric, not transitive   (iii) Not transitive   (v) Equivalence relation

*13. $A \times B \times C = \{(x, y, z) \mid x \in A, y \in B, z \in C\}$,
$A_1 \times A_2 \times \cdots \times A_n = \{(x_1, x_2, \ldots, x_n) \mid x_1 \in A_1, x_2 \in A_2,$
$\ldots, x_n \in A_n\}$

Section 4–2

1. Statements   Open sentences
(a) Statement   (b) The variable is "x."
(d) Statement   (c) The variable is "He."
(e) Statement   (f) The variables are "She" and "I."

3. (a) $\{\sqrt{2}\}$ (c) $\{2\}$ (e) $\{1\}$

Section 4–3

1. (a), (c), (d), (f)

3. (a) $(1, 2)$ is a subset of F. Incorrect. $(1, 2)$ is not a set and only a set can be a subset of a set.
(c) 2 is in the relation ρ to 3 is equivalent to $(3, 2)$ belongs to ρ. Incorrect. $2 \rho 3 \leftrightarrow (2, 3) \in \rho$ or $3 \rho 2 \leftrightarrow (3, 2) \in \rho$.
(e) x is in the relation F to $F(x)$. Correct. The ordered pair $(x, F(x))$ belongs to F.

5. (b), (c), (e), (f), (h)

7. (a) 0   (c) -4 (e) 0   (g) $2hx + h^2$

9. $D = \{x \mid x \text{ is a statement}\}$; $R = \{T, F\}$

11. Yes.

Section 4–4

1. (a)   (c)   (e)

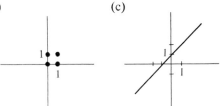

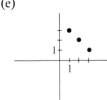

*3. (a)   (c)   (e)

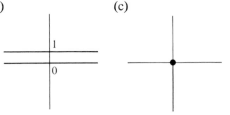

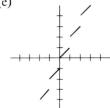

+5. (b), (c), (d)

7. The proof is to be carried out by considering 4 cases:

I $\quad a \geq 0, b \geq 0; \quad |a| = a, |b| = b, |ab| = ab$

II $\quad a \geq 0, b < 0; \quad |a| = a, |b| = -b, |ab| = -ab$

III $\quad a < 0, b \geq 0; \quad |a| = -a, |b| = b, |ab| = -ab$

IV $\quad a < 0, b < 0; \quad |a| = -a, |b| = -b, |ab| = ab$

The proof is obvious for each case.

Section 4–5

1. (a) $\{(x, -x + 1)\}$
(c) $\{(x, y) \mid x = y^2 \wedge y < 0\}$ or $\{(y, x) \mid y = x^2 \wedge x < 0\}$
(e) x is the husband of y or y is the wife of x.
(g) y is a sibling of x.

3. Functions: (a), (b), (c), (d); (e) in a monogamous society.
Converse relations which are functions: (a), (b), (c), (d); (e) in a monogamous society.
Converse relations which are inverse functions: (a), (b), (c), (d), (e).

5. (a)

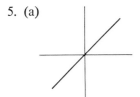

Inverse function is the same as the original function.

(c)

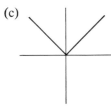

No inverse

(e)

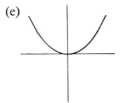

No inverse

Section 4–6

1. (a) $f + g = \{(x, 2)\}; \quad f - g = \{(x, -2)\}; \quad f \cdot g = \{(x, 0)\};$
$f/g = \{(x, 0)\}$
(c) $f + g = \{(x, 4)\}; \quad f - g = \{(x, 4x)\};$
$f \cdot g = \{(x, 4(1 - x^2))\}; \quad f/g = \left\{\left(x, \dfrac{1 + x}{1 - x}\right) \,\middle|\, x \neq 1\right\}$

(e) $f + g = \{(0, 0)\}$; $f - g = \{(0, 0)\}$; $f \cdot g = \{(0, 0)\}$; $f/g = \emptyset$

3. (a)

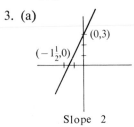

Slope 2

(c)

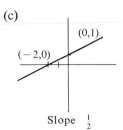

Slope $\frac{1}{2}$

5. (a) $\{(x, 2x)\}$ (c) $\{x, \frac{1}{2}(x + 1)\}$ (e) $\{(x, 3x)\}$

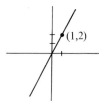 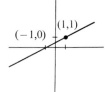 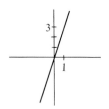

+7. $\left\{\left(x, -\dfrac{b}{a}x + b\right)\right\}$, if $a \neq 0$.   9. $\{(x, 2x)\}$

11. No. The slope is 0.

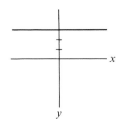

Section 4–7

1. (a) $I^2 f + gI + f = \{(x, 2x^2 - x + 2)\}$, degree two
(c) $I^2 + 2I - f = \{(x, x^2 + 2x - 2)\}$, degree two

3. The degree of the sum polynomial $\leq$ the degree of the addend polynomial of largest degree.

5. Yes. It is a polynomial of degree one.

+7. (a) $(-\frac{1}{2}, \frac{3}{4})$ (c) $(0, -1)$ (e) $(0, 1)$

9. $p(-x) = a(-x)^2 + b = p(x)$

Review Exercises

1. $\{0, 2\}$ 3. Yes. $D = \{0, 1, 2, 3\}, R = \{1, 2, 3\}$.

5. (a)

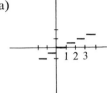

7. Inverse defined by $y = 2x$.

(a)   (b)

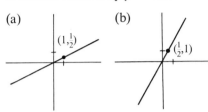

9. $\{(x, \frac{5}{2}x - \frac{1}{2})\}$

CHAPTER 5

Section 5–1

3. (a) $2, 1, \frac{1}{2}, \frac{1}{4}, \frac{1}{8}$ (c) $-1, 1, -1, 1, -1$ (e) $2, \frac{3}{2}, \frac{4}{3}, \frac{5}{4}, \frac{6}{5}$

5. $1, 1, 2, 3, 5, 8, 13, 21, 34, 55$ 9. $\$1,218.99$

Section 5–2

1. (a) $2, 4, 8, 16, 32$ (c) $0, 1, 0, 1, 0$
   (e) $3, 5, 7, 9, 11$ (g) $2, 2, \frac{8}{3}, 4, \frac{32}{5}$

3. $L = 1, N = 10$ 5. Has no limit.

Section 5–3

1. (a) $\frac{7}{5}, \frac{141}{100}, \frac{707}{500}$ (c) $3, \frac{22}{7}, \frac{31}{10}$

3. (a) $0.\overline{285714}$ (c) $0.\overline{6}$

5. (a) $\frac{14}{99}$ (c) $\frac{374}{333}$ (e) $\frac{41}{990}$

Section 5–4

1. (a) $[1, 3]$ (c) $\emptyset$ (e) $\{-1, 3\}$

(g) $\overline{A}$, where $A = \,]0, 4[$ (i) $[1, 5]$

3. (a), (b), (c)

*5. If $\begin{cases} x > 0 & \text{limit} = 1; \\ x = 0 & \text{limit does not exist}; \\ x < 0 & \text{limit} = -1. \end{cases}$

Review Exercises

1. $2, \frac{9}{4}, \frac{64}{9}, \frac{625}{256}$

3. (a) 0   (c) 3   (e) Divergent   (g) 2

5. $0.\overline{538461}$ 7. $f(a)$

CHAPTER 6

Section 6–2

1. $\{(x, 0)\}$ 3. $\{(x, 1)\}$ 5. $\{(x, 2)\}$

7. $\{(x, 2ax)\}$ 9. $\{(x, 8x + 5)\}$

*11. $Df(x) = 0$ for all x, x not an integer

13. $y - 2 = 6(x - 1)$ 15. $\{(x, x^2)\}$

Section 6–3

1. 0 ft/sec, 64 ft/sec

3. $t = \dfrac{\sqrt{15}}{2}$, $16\sqrt{15}$ ft/sec   5. $DV(x) = 20\pi x - \pi x^2$

Section 6–4

1. Minimum at $(0, -1)$. Always concave upward.

3. Maximum at $(0, 0)$; minimum at $(\pm\frac{1}{2}\sqrt{2}, -\frac{1}{4})$. Concave downward $]-1/\sqrt{6}, 1/\sqrt{6}[$; concave upward $[-1/\sqrt{6}, 1/\sqrt{6}]$.

5. Maximum at $(2/\sqrt{3}, 16/3\sqrt{3})$; minimum at $(-2/\sqrt{3}, -16/3\sqrt{3})$. Concave upward $x < 0$; concave downward $x > 0$.

7. Minimum at $(2, -4)$; maximum at $(-2, 28)$. Concave upward $x > 0$; concave downward $x < 0$.

9. 25×25

11. $L = W$

13. $3, \$9000$

Section 6–5

1. (a) 15   (c) 100   3. (a) 2   5. 0

7. (a) 1   (c) $-\frac{1}{6}$

Section 6–6

3. $\dfrac{1}{h}\displaystyle\int_x^{x+h} f.$

5. (a) $\{(x, c)\}$ (c) $\{(x, cx)\}$ (e) $\{(x, x^3/3)\}$
   (g) $\{(x, 2x^3/3)\}$ (i) $\{(x, x^{n+1}/(n+1))\}$

Section 6–7

1. 16   3. $625{,}000\pi$ 5. $\pi/5,\ \pi/2$

Review Exercises

3. (a) 1   (c) m 5. 2   7. 3 sec, 114 ft

9. $y = 3x + 1$ 11. $34\frac{1}{2}$ 13. $73\frac{1}{2}$

15. Maximum at $(-1, 7)$; minimum at $(2, -20)$; $3\frac{1}{2}$

CHAPTER 7

Section 7–1

1. 10; 3; 1; 30,240; 120; 6.

3. (a) 53,130   (c) 14,190   (e) $\dfrac{52!}{13!39!}$.

5. 320   7. 45; 120   9. 54

Section 7–2

1. (a) 16   3. $\dfrac{27!}{13!14!}$

5. The $(n + 1)$st row contains the coefficients of the terms in the expansion of $(a + b)^n$.

Section 7–3

3. $\frac{2}{9}$ 5. $\frac{25}{52}$ 7. 1

Review Exercises

1. 210   3. 96   5. $26^2 \cdot 10^4$ 7. $\dfrac{19!}{13!6!}$

CHAPTER 8

Section 8–2

1. (a) No. $a' \notin S.$ (c) No. $0' \notin S.$ (e) Yes.
(g) Yes.   (i) No. Not closed.

3.

$\circ$	I	R_1	R_2
I	I	R_1	R_2
R_1	R_1	R_2	I
R_2	R_2	I	R_1

Yes.

5. Yes. $f_1' = f_1$, $f_4' = f_6$, $f_6' = f_4$.   7. The solution is $a' \circ b$.
9. $a^1 = a$, $a^n = a^{n-1} \circ a$.   11. $\{I, R_2\}$.

13. No. The even integers with the operation of addition are a cyclic group but the group has infinitely many elements.

Section 8–3

5. Use B_2 with z' replacing a.   11.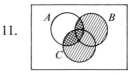

////// $B \cup C$

▨▨▨ $A \cap (B \cup C)$

////// $A \cap C$

\\\\\ $A \cap B$

Shaded points $(A \cap B) \cup (A \cap C)$

Section 8–4

3.

p	$\vee$	q	$\leftrightarrow$	q	$\vee$	p
T	T	T	T	T	T	T
T	T	F	T	F	T	T
F	T	T	T	T	T	F
F	F	F	T	F	F	F
1	3	2	**4**	2	3	1

▲

7.

a	b	c	a	$\wedge$	$(b$	$\vee$	$c)$	$\leftrightarrow$	$(a$	$\wedge$	$b)$	$\vee$	$(a$	$\wedge$	$c)$
T	T	T	T	T	T	T	T	T	T	T	T	T	T	T	T
T	T	F	T	T	T	T	F	T	T	T	T	T	T	F	F
T	F	T	T	T	F	T	T	T	T	F	F	T	T	T	T
T	F	F	T	F	F	F	F	T	T	F	F	F	T	F	F
F	T	T	F	F	T	T	T	T	F	F	T	F	F	F	T
F	T	F	F	F	T	T	F	T	F	F	T	F	F	F	F
F	F	T	F	F	F	T	T	T	F	F	F	F	F	F	T
F	F	F	F	F	F	F	F	T	F	F	F	F	F	F	F
1	2	3	1	5	2	4	3	**9**	1	6	2	8	1	7	3

▲

9. $\sim(a \wedge b) \leftrightarrow \sim a \vee \sim b$
   $\sim(a \vee b) \leftrightarrow \sim a \wedge \sim b$

11. (a) $(a + b' + d)(a + b + c')(a + c + d)$
    (c) $(a + b)(c + a') + b(c' + b')$

Section 8–5

1. (a) Not a field since multiplicative inverses are missing.
   (c) Not a field since multiplicative inverses are missing.
   (e) This is a field.
   (g) This is a field

3. Yes.

5.

+	0	1	2	3	4
0	0	1	2	3	4
1	1	2	3	4	0
2	2	3	4	0	1
3	2	4	0	1	2
4	4	0	1	2	3

×	0	1	2	3	4
0	0	0	0	0	0
1	0	1	2	3	4
2	0	2	4	1	3
3	0	3	1	4	2
4	0	4	3	2	1

INDEX

Abelian, 162, 163, 166, 179
Abscissa, 80
Absolute value, 81
Acceleration, 121
Addition, 47, 183
  Boolean algebra, 173
  field, 179, 183
  natural number, 47
  rational number, 59
Algebra of sets, 171
Analytic geometry, 79
Antecedent, 24
Antiderivative, 134–135
Application, 32, 120, 122, 135–139,
  153, 156, 174–178
Approximation, 128, 181
Arc length, 137, 138
Archimedes (287?–212 B.C.), 133
Area, 127–133
Arithmetic, 46
Arithmetic progression, 51, 96
Arrangements, 143, 144
Associative, 160, 163, 165, 172, 180
Average rate of change, 119
Average speed, 119
Axioms, 19, 20, 29–32, 64, 156–183
  Boolean algebra, 167
  field, 179
  group, 160
  logic, 30
  Peano's, 47
  probability, 150
  systems, 156-185
Axis, 79

Belongs to, 3, 5, 29, 156, 159, 160, 167
Biconditional statement, 26
Binary, 67, 160, 167, 179
Binomial coefficient, 148
Binomial theorem, 146–149, 154
Boole, George (1815–1864), 166
Boolean algebra, 166–178
Bounded, 106

Calculus, 114–142, 167
Cancellation Law, 161
Cartesian product, 67, 71

Circle, 115, 127
  tangent to, 115
Circuit, 176
Class. 156
Closed, 52, 58, 107, 175
  interval, 107
  switch, 175
Closure, 160
Collinear, 29
Combination, 143–149, 153
Commutative, 162, 167, 172
Complement, 9, 10, 167, 170, 172
  of a set, 9, 10
Complete, 182
Complex numbers, 182
Composition of functions, 164
Compound statements, 21
Concave, 126
Conclusion, 24, 33
Conditional statement, 24–28
Conjunction, 20
Consequent, 24
Constant, 71–73, 91
  function, 86, 87, 91
Contain, 156
Continuity, at a point, 109
  in an interval, 109
Contradiction, 35
  proof by, 38
Contrapositive, 26
Converges, 101
Converse, 26, 84–86
  of a function, 84
  of a relation, 84–86
Convex, 29
Coordinates, 80
Correspondence, 13, 75, 174
  one-to-one, 13, 14
Counterexample, 39
Counting, 47, 143–155
Counting numbers, 143
Curve tracing, 122–127
Cut, Dedekind, 62–63
Cyclic, 166

Decimal, 102–106
  nonrepeating, 106

repeating, 103–105
terminating, 103, 105
Decreasing function, 123
Dedekind cut, 62
Dedekind, Richard (1831–1916), 66
Definite integral, 130–141
Definition, 29–32
  recursive, 47
Degree of polynomial, 92
De Morgan's Laws, 12
Dependent variable, 77
Derivative, 116–127, 135, 140
Descartes, René (1596–1650), 79, 133
Detachment, Rule of, 34, 35
Diagram, Venn, 10–12, 172
Difference, 53
  of rational numbers, 59
Direct proof, 35–37
Disjoint sets, 8, 150
Disjunction, 20–21
  exclusive, 21
  inclusive, 21
Distance, 108
Distributive, 167, 172
Diverges, 101
Divisibility, 49
Division, 179
  by zero, 57
Domain, 69, 77, 80–82, 84
  of a function, 77
  of a relation, 69, 84
Dual, 167
Duality, 167

Electrical networks, 174–178
Element, 5, 160, 167
Empty set, 4, 8, 9
Equal, 36
  cuts, 63
  integers, 51
  rational numbers, 57
  sets, 7, 171
  subclasses, 158
Equivalence relations, 70, 167, 171, 172
Equivalent networks, 175
Equivalent sets, 14
Euclid (about 300 B.C.), 38
Euclidean geometry, 31, 88
Euler, Leonard (1707–1783), 77
Even number, 14, 36

Event, 150, 151
Exclusive disjunction, 21

Factorial, 51, 144
Fermat, Pierre de (1601–1665), 133
Fibonacci, Leonardo (1175–c.1250), 97
Fibonacci sequence, 97–99
Field, 178–183
  complete ordered, 182
  finite, 180, 181, 183
  generators, 179
  of quotients, 179
  ordered, 181, 182
Finite sets, 14–15
Force, 136
Fraction, 57
Frege, L. F. G. (1848–1925), 46
Frequency, 152–153
Function, 73–93, 107–110
  absolute value, 81
  composition of, 164
  constant, 86
  continuous, 109
  decreasing, 123
  derivative, 116
  domain of, 74
  greatest integer, 81, 110
  identity, 80
  increasing, 123
  inverse, 84–86
  limit of, 107
  linear, 86–90, 109
  polynomial, 91–93, 109
  probability, 151–152
  quadratic, 91, 122
  range of, 74
  rational, 109
  square root, 82
  stationary, 123
Fundamental theorem of integral calculus, 131, 133–135

Generalization, 24, 147, 150
Generator, 166, 179
Geometry, 29–32, 79, 88, 159
  analytic, 79
  Cartesian, 79
  Euclidean, 31, 88
Geometric progression, 97, 104
Graph, 79–83, 109, 116, 122–126
  of inverse, 84–86

of linear function, 86–90
of polynomial, 91–93
of the tangent, 116
Greatest integer function, 81, 110
Group, 160–166
  abelian, 162
  commutative, 162
  identity, 160
  inverse, 179
  permutation, 163–165
  rotations, 162

Hypothesis, 24, 35

Idempotent, 168
Identity elements, of a Boolean algebra, 167
  of a field, 179
  of a group, 160
Identity function, 80, 87, 91
If and only if, 26
Inclusive disjunction, 21
Incommensurables, 61
Increasing function, 123
Increment, 120
Independent variable, 77
Indirect proof, 37–39
Induction, mathematical, 49–51, 96, 98
Inference, Rule of, 34, 36
Infinite sets, 14–15
Infinite sequences, 95–112
Infinity, 101
Integers, 51–56, 60, 162
Integral, definite, 130–141
Interest, compound, 97
Intersection of sets, 8, 171, 172
Interval, closed, 107
  open, 107
Inverse, 84–86
  of a field, 180
  of a function, 84
  of a group, 160-161
  logical, 29
Irrational number, 63, 103, 110, 181

Kronecker, Leopold (1823–1891), 46

Label, 21, 23
Leibniz, Gottfried Wilhelm (1646–1716), 133

Less than, 55, 58, 60, 69
Liber abaci, 97–98
Limit, of a function, 107
  of a sequence, 99–102, 182
Limiting position, 116
Line, 29, 30, 31, 32, 88, 159
  slope of, 80, 90, 116
Linear function, 86–90, 109
Logic, 19–44, 64, 174
Logical equivalence, 23, 27

Mapping, 75
Marginal revenue, 120, 122
Matching, 13
Mathematical induction, 49–51
Mathematical systems, 156–185
Maximum, 135
  relative, 124, 126
Member of a set, 3, 4, 5, 156
Minimum, 135
  relative, 124, 126
Model, mathematical, 31
Modus ponens, 34
Modus tollens, 35
Multiplication, Boolean algebra, 173
  field, 179, 183
  group, 163
  of natural numbers, 47
  of rational numbers, 59

Natural numbers, 13–15, 46–56, 60, 64, 65, 95, 162, 165, 178
Necessary, 25, 29, 126
Negation of a statement, 20, 23, 28, 41, 42
Negative integer, 53, 55
Network, electrical, 174–178
Newton, Sir Isaac (1642–1727), 133
Nondecreasing, 106
Nonempty, 14
Null set, 4
Number line, 59, 63
Number systems, 46–66, 178
Numbers, 46–66
  complex, 182
  even, 14, 36
  irrational, 63, 103, 110, 181
  natural, 13–15, 46–56, 60, 64–65, 95, 162, 165, 178
  negative, 53, 55
  odd, 37

rational, 56–60, 64, 102–110, 163, 179–181
real, 64, 102–110, 151, 181
transcendental, 63

Odd number, 37
One-to-one correspondence, 13, 14
Only if, 25
Open interval, 107
Open sentence, 71–73, 107
Open switch, 175–176
Operations, 67, 160, 162, 167, 173, 179
    on sets, 5–10
Ordered field, 181, 182
Ordered pair, 52, 55, 57, 67, 79, 95, 164
Ordinate, 80
Origin, 80

Parabola, 91
Parallel, 174
Pascal, Blaise (1623–1666), 149
Pascal's triangle, 149
Peano, G. (1858–1932), 46
Peano's axioms, 47–51, 54
Permutations, 143–146, 163-165
Point, 29–32, 79, 88, 159
Polynomial, 91–93
    degree of, 92
    root of, 92
    zero of, 92
Positive, 55, 181
Postulates, 30
Power set, 9
Premise, 33
Pressure, water, 136
Prime(s), 38
Probability, 143–155
    assignment of, 151–153
    axioms for, 150
    function, 151–152
Product; *see* Multiplication
Progression, arithmetic, 51, 96
    geometric, 51, 97
Proof, 33
    by contradiction, 38
    direct, 35
    formal, 35, 36
    indirect, 37

methods of, 35–39
    reductio ad absurdum, 38
Proper subset, 10, 15
Pythagoras, theorem of, 60

Quadrant, 80
Quadratic, 91, 122
Quantifier, existential, 41–42
    universal, 41–42
Quotients, 58, 59, 179

Range, 69, 71, 74, 84–86
    of a function, 74
    of a relation, 69, 71, 84–86
    of a variable, 71
Rate of change, 122
Rational function, 92
Rational number, 56–60, 64, 102–110, 163, 179–181
    difference of, 59
    product of, 59
    quotient of, 59
    sum of, 59
Real number, 60–64, 102–110, 151, 181
Recursion formula, 96
Recursive definition, 47, 48, 96
Reductio ad absurdum, 38
Reflexive, 70
Relation, 67–86
    domain of, 69
    equivalence, 70
    range of, 69, 71
Relations between sets, 5–10
Repeating decimal, 103–105
Replacement, Rule of, 34
Ring, 183
Root of a polynomial, 92
Roster notation, 4
Rotation, 162
Russell, Bertrand (1872–   ), 1, 30, 46, 184

Sample space, 150, 153
Segment, 29, 88, 90
Sequence, 95–112
    arithmetic, 96
    bounded, 106
    converges, 101
    diverges, 101
    Fibonacci, 97–99

general term, 96
geometric, 97
limit of, 99–102
terms of, 95, 96
Series, switches connected in, 174
Sets, 3–17, 46–66, 71–72, 75–76, 160, 174
empty, 4, 8, 9, 146, 147, 149, 150, 156, 166–167
equal, 7, 158, 171
equivalent, 14
finite, 14, 15
infinite, 14, 15
member of, 3, 4, 5, 156
null, 4, 150, 172
power, 9
solution, 72, 107–108
universal, 4, 8, 150, 172
Slope, of a line, 90, 116
of a line segment, 88
Solution set, 72, 107–108
Speed, 121
average, 119
instantaneous, 119
Square root, 82
Statement, 19–28, 31–39, 40–42, 71, 72, 149, 167, 174
biconditional, 26
compound, 21
conditional, 24–28
conjunction, 20
contradiction, 35
contrapositive, 26
converse, 26, 84–86
disjunction, 20
dual, 167
negation, 20, 23, 28, 41, 42
quantified, 40–43
tautology, 26, 34, 35
Stationary, 123
Stone, Marshall H. (1903–   ), 172
Straight line; see Line
Structure, 156, 165, 171, 179, 182
Subclass, 156–159
Subfield, 180
Subgroup, 166
Subscript, 38, 95
Subset, 7, 49, 146–147, 166, 172, 180
Subtraction, 179
Successor, 47

Sufficient, 25, 29, 126
Sum, lower, 128–131
upper, 128–131
Syllogism, Law of, 34, 35, 37
Symbolic logic, 19
Symmetric, 70, 83, 171
with respect to the y-axis, 83
Systems, 30, 184

Tangent, 114–118, 133
to a circle, 115
Tautology, 26, 34, 35
Terminating decimal, 103, 105
Terms of a sequence, 95, 96
Theorem, 29–32, 184
Theory, 31, 32, 171
Transitive, 70
Truth table, 20–27, 34
Truth value, 22

Undefined terms, 30, 47, 64, 88, 156, 160, 167, 184
for Boolean algebra, 167
for geometry, 30
for groups, 160
Union, 8, 171, 172
Universal set, 4, 8, 150, 172
Universe of discourse, 4, 150

Valid argument, 33
Value, 71, 151
Variable, 71–73, 77
dependent, 77
independent, 77
Velocity, 121
Venn diagrams, 10–12, 172
Vertex of a parabola, 93
Volume, 138–139

Whitehead, Alfred North (1861–1947), 46
Work, 138

x-axis, 79

y-axis, 79

Zero, 53, 57
Zero of a polynomial, 92